GW00580244

REWARD

REWARD

Upper-intermediate

Practice Book

Diana Pye
Simon Greenall

Heinemann

English... at home and abroad

VOCABULARY

1 📼 Listen to people speaking six different languages. Write down words or phrases which you would use to describe how these languages sound to you. Here are some ideas.

guttural sing-song mysterious (un)familiar
strange incomprehensible noisy harsh
emotional emotionless angry complicated
rapid monotonous (un)attractive excited
serious melodious exotic romantic alien
high-pitched emphatic gentle

1 _____
2 _____
3 _____
4 _____
5 _____
6 _____

2 📼 Can you guess which languages they are? Listen again and put the number of the speaker by the language. There are two extra languages.

☐ Spanish   ☐ Chinese
☐ Japanese   ☐ Italian
☐ French   ☐ Russian
☐ Welsh   ☐ German

3 Put these words in order and make questions about the languages.

1 any you do of languages these speak?

   _____

2 to you them learn like any of would?

   _____

3 particularly you which think are to difficult do learn?

   _____

4 native any of languages are to these your similar language?

   _____

5 long learning been you how have English?

   _____

6 school languages you what did study at?

   _____

4 Write answers to the questions in activity 3.

1 _____
2 _____
3 _____
4 _____
5 _____
6 _____

LISTENING

1 📼 Listen to two people discussing various languages. Write down the languages they mention and the words or phrases they use to describe them.

Language   **Description**

_____
_____
_____
_____
_____
_____

2 📼 Listen again and complete these sentences with a question and/or a tag.

1 Some people are so lucky, _____?
2 Well, at least you can understand written French, _____?
3 I love listening to people speaking it, _____?
4 The trouble is, you have to make such an effort to learn another language, _____?
5 I'd love to be able to speak it, _____?
6 _____ go to classes together, _____?

3 Put a tick (✓) by the statements which are true.

1 The woman speaks French fluently.

2 The man studied French and Spanish at school.

3 The man did a year's Japanese at college.

4 The woman would like to learn Japanese.

5 Neither of them has studied Arabic.

6 Both of them need German for their work.

4 Write sentences correcting the statements in activity 3 which are not true.

_____

_____

_____

_____

_____

_____

_____

_____

GRAMMAR

1 Complete these sentences with a suitable question tag.

1 Let's go on a course together, _____?

2 You couldn't lend me your book, _____?

3 Don't be too angry with him, _____?

4 There won't be too many people, _____?

5 She looks very well, _____?

6 Hold this for a moment, _____?

7 There aren't any spare cassettes, _____?

8 You can't come with me, _____?

9 You haven't been to the States, _____?

10 There isn't anyone at the office today, _____?

2 Respond to these statements with a question.

1 It's only ten o'clock.
Oh, _____? Well, we can stay a bit longer, then.

2 I've done enough work for today.
_____? That's good.

3 I'd love a cup of coffee.
_____? I'll get you one.

4 They're going to live in Greece.
_____ really? How marvellous!

5 By the way, the police caught the burglar.
_____? That's a relief.

6 I haven't met the new neighbours yet.
_____? They're charming.

3 Write questions you could ask another person on your English course.

1 When _____

_____

2 How often _____

_____

3 How long _____

_____

4 Could _____

_____

5 Have _____

_____

6 Where _____

_____

7 Who _____

_____

8 Did _____

_____

9 Why _____

_____

10 How far _____

_____

SOUNDS

1 🔲 Listen to the sentences in *Listening* activity 2 and decide which are real questions. Say the sentences aloud.

2 🔲 Listen and repeat the sentences in *Grammar* activity 1.

3 🔲 Listen and repeat the phrases below. Notice how the underlined consonant is not pronounced.

I<u>s</u> she Japanese?   Doe<u>s</u> she?   becau<u>se</u> she likes

don'<u>t</u> stay   doesn'<u>t</u> want   don'<u>t</u> go   can'<u>t</u> stay

won'<u>t</u> pay   mustn'<u>t</u> wait   weren'<u>t</u> there

READING

1 Read the passage *Learning styles: the reluctant learner* and put a tick (✓) by the sentence which best summarises the problem described in the passage.

1 It is very difficult to study and work or follow courses all day.

2 It's not easy to discipline yourself to study efficiently at home.

3 Most people who go to evening classes find it difficult to work at home.

4 There are a lot of things more interesting than learning a language.

2 What five excuses not to study does the person find?

1 _____

2 _____

3 _____

4 _____

5 _____

3 Answer the questions and try to guess the meanings of the words or phrases.

1 *browses through the newspaper* Does he
a) study the newspaper carefully or
b) leisurely look through it?

2 *hovers over his desk* Does he
a) stand by his desk or
b) does he sit down?

3 *pangs of hunger* Is this
a) a physical sensation or
b) a mental state?

4 *drowsiness* Does he feel
a) physically uncomfortable or
b) sleepy?

WRITING

1 Write advice for the reluctant learner described in the passage.

_____
_____
_____
_____
_____
_____
_____
_____
_____
_____

2 Write a short passage describing how you work or study. Do you ever make excuses to yourself like the reluctant learner?

_____
_____
_____
_____
_____
_____
_____
_____
_____
_____
_____

Learning styles:
the reluctant learner

My friend Tom is one of those Six-o'clock-In-The-Evening-Enthusiastic-Determined-And-Well-Intentioned-Studier-Until-Midnight types. At six o'clock he approaches his desk, and carefully organises everything in preparation for the study period to follow. Having everything in place he next carefully adjusts each item again, giving him time to complete the first excuse; he recalls that in the morning he did not have quite enough time to read all the items of interest in the newspaper. He also realises that if he is going to study it is best to have such small items completely out of the way before settling down to the task at hand.

He therefore leaves his desk, browses through the newspaper and notices that there are more articles of interest than he had originally thought. He also notices, as he leafs through the pages, the entertainment section. At this point it will seem like a good idea to plan for the evening's first break – perhaps an interesting programme between 8 and 8.30 pm.

He finds the programme, and it inevitably starts at about 7 pm.

At this point, he thinks 'Well, I've had a difficult day and it's not too long before the programme starts, and I need a rest anyway and the relaxation will help me to get down to studying ...' He returns to his desk at 7.45 pm, because the beginning of the next programme was also a bit more interesting than he thought it would be.

At this stage, he still hovers over his desk tapping his book reassuringly as he remembers that phone call to a friend which is best cleared out of the way before the serious studying begins.

The phone call, of course, is much more interesting and longer than originally planned, but eventually the intrepid studier finds himself back at his desk at about 8.30 pm.

At this point in the proceedings he actually sits down at his desk, opens the book with a display of physical determination and starts to read (usually page one) as he experiences the first pangs of hunger and thirst. This is disastrous because he realises that the longer he waits to satisfy the pangs, the worse they will get, and the more interrupted his study concentration will be. The obvious and only solution is a light snack, but as more and more tasty items come to mind, the snack becomes a feast.

Having removed this final object, the desk is returned to with the certain knowledge that this time there is nothing that could possibly interfere with the dedication. The first couple of sentences on page one are looked at again ... as the studier realises that his stomach is feeling decidedly heavy and a general drowsiness seems to have set in. Far better at this juncture to watch that other interesting half-hour programme at 10 o'clock, after which the digestion will be mostly completed and the rest will enable him really to get down to work.

At 12 o'clock we find him asleep in front of the TV.

Even at this point he will think that things have not gone too badly, for after all he had a good rest, a good meal, watched some interesting and relaxing programmes, fulfilled his social commitments to his friends, digested the day's information, and got everything completely out of the way so that tomorrow, at 6 o'clock ...

2 Friends and relations

VOCABULARY

1 Find twenty-three verbs in the puzzle. They go in two directions (→) and (↓). Some letters can be used more than once.

B	O	W	K	I	S	S	N	O	D
E	K	N	E	E	L	W	A	V	E
C	L	A	P	C	U	D	D	L	E
K	A	S	M	I	L	E	B	F	S
O	U	H	W	H	S	S	L	R	C
N	G	R	I	N	P	T	O	O	R
C	H	U	N	S	I	A	W	W	A
H	U	G	K	P	T	R	X	N	T
E	G	S	H	A	K	E	E	O	C
W	Z	A	S	T	R	E	T	C	H

2 Complete the sentences below using verbs from the puzzle. You may have to change the form of some of the verbs.

1 It was so funny I burst out _____.
2 He _____ his head in agreement.
3 In Britain you _____ hands when you are introduced to someone for the first time.
4 For some reason the man at the table opposite had been _____ at us rudely since we arrived.
5 The meat was so tough we had to _____ it for ages.
6 He _____ his shoulders and walked away because there was nothing he could do.
7 In some countries it is unacceptable to _____ your nose in public.
8 The Japanese _____ to one another as a form of greeting.
9 The little boy _____ cheekily at us before running off.
10 She _____ warmly when she recognised us.

SOUNDS

1 Look at these words. Underline the /ʃ/ sounds and circle the /tʃ/ sounds.

cheek chew convention couchette exchange friendship pinch scratch shake shrug social suspicious

🔊 Listen and check.

2 Look at the sentences. When is the 'r' silent and when is it used as a link? Mark the 'r' links and cross out the silent 'r' where appropriate.

1 Don't point your finger at people.
2 Only use the familiar form for friends.
3 He lives far away.
4 It's still quite far to go.
5 We bought it for ourselves.
6 She's taller than her mother.
7 They left a quarter of an hour ago.
8 You'll discover that they're very courteous.
9 Is it near here?
10 Poor Anne, you are unlucky!
11 Don't stare like that!

🔊 Listen and check. Say the phrases aloud.

3 Can you work out the rule for the silent 'r' and the linking 'r'?

4 Match the words with the same vowel sound.

frown	blow
stare	arm
born	bow
though	foot
warm	yawn
put	bear
laugh	form

🔊 Listen and check.

GRAMMAR

1 Complete the grammar rules by matching the two parts of the sentences. There may be more than one answer.

1 You don't use any article ☐ ☐ ☐ ☐
2 You use a definite article ☐ ☐ ☐ ☐
3 You use an indefinite article ☐ ☐ ☐ ☐

a with plural nouns.
b when you talk about something for the first time.
c with abstract nouns.
d after *be* before jobs.
e when you talk about something again.
f with nouns defined by a phrase or a clause.
g for most countries.

2 Here are examples of each of the rules in activity 1 above. Match the rules (a to g) with the examples that illustrate them.

1 We had trouble getting there.
2 She is a health food expert.
3 I went home to get the book I had told him about.
4 I spent six years in France before moving to Greece.
5 He has made friends at his new school.
6 Here's the book I told you about.
7 I bought a new car and I drove it home.

3 Complete these sentences with an article or zero article.

1 It is very important to have (1) _____ varied diet and not to eat (2) _____ unhealthy food.
2 (3) _____ time is (4) _____ money.
3 (5) _____ money they earn is well-deserved.
4 They tried to keep out of (6) _____ trouble.
5 We had (7) _____ fun at the camp.
6 (8) _____ psychologists study (9) _____ human behaviour.
7 (10) _____ rank is (11) _____ all-important factor.
8 He has (12) _____ passion for (13) _____ football.
9 I made (14) _____ terrible mistake.
10 (15) _____ familiarity breeds (16) _____ contempt.

READING

1 Write down as many ways of greeting people as you can think of.

_____

2 Read passage A on page 8 and find out how the Japanese usually greet one another. Why do foreigners find this greeting difficult?

_____

3 Find four things you can do wrong when you bow to someone.

1 _____
2 _____
3 _____
4 _____

4 What determines how you bow to someone?

_____

_____

5 Read passage B on page 8 and find out what sort of greetings it is about.

6 Which countries have greetings which the writer describes as:

romantic? _____
unromantic? _____
diffident? _____
affectionate? _____
simple and effective? _____

Which countries have greetings based on:

health? _____
religion? _____

7 In British English when would you ask these questions? Answer the questions.

1 How do you do? _____
2 How are you? _____

8 Why was the Australian shop assistant surprised by the English person's response to the greeting: *'Hi! How are you today?'*

9 How do you greet people in your country?

A   A quarter of an hour in Japan will convince you that you are among exquisitely well-mannered people. You will, of course, immediately notice their habit of bowing. Everybody keeps bowing. Everybody keeps bowing to everybody else with a great deal of natural and inimitable grace. Bowing is neither less nor more silly than shaking hands or kissing the cheek, but it is quainter, more formal, more oriental; it is also infectious. After a few hours you start bowing yourself. But you bow too deeply or not deeply enough; you bow to the wrong person at the wrong time. You'll discover that the Japanese have a complicated hierarchy in bowing: who bows to whom, how deeply and for how long. One of the American states had an early traffic law which laid down that if two cars met at an intersection, neither was to move before the other had gone. Similarly, if two Japanese bow, neither is to straighten up before the other stands erect in front of him. A little complicated to us; they manage it without difficulty and even the smallest difference in rank, standing, age, social position will be subtly reflected in that split second one person's bow is shorter than the other's.

B   Last year, soon after I arrived in Australia, I was in a shop where the assistant greeted me with a cheery: 'Hi! How are you today?'
Fooled, no doubt by jet lag, into thinking her inquiry was in earnest, I said: 'Actually, I'm shattered. I've just flown in from London.' The shop assistant, not expecting an answer, was speechless.

Greetings have become such an intrinsic part of our daily lives that they often no longer mean anything. In some places, however, the culture of address is taken very seriously. In parts of Africa, paying your compliments can take a long time. A friend of mine, stranded in Timbuktu without any petrol, needed an hour to ask the local mayor about the health of his family before he could even approach the issue of refuelling his car.
Health is also the key question in Ukraine and Russia, where friends greet each other with *zdoroven'ki buli*, (let's be healthy), or *zdorova*, wishing the other person good health. This is often accompanied by handshaking and kisses on the cheek.

It should come as no surprise that the romantic French gush *enchantée*, literally 'I'm enchanted', on being introduced – but then even the more sombre Hungarians offer the affectionate *Kezét csokolom* (I kiss your hands) when a man greets a woman.

Some nationalities are more orientated towards religion in their approach. Protestant northern Germans greet according to the time of day, but their Catholic southern counterparts, and some Austrians, say *Grüss Gott*, (greet God). On Mount Athos in Greece the monks say 'Greetings, Father.' No feminine greeting is necessary as women are not allowed there.

The British and the Italians have a flair for diffident salutations. Italians are surprisingly unromantic. They may say *piacere* (delighted to meet you) or on special occasions *onorato* (I am honoured).

The British, with their characteristic reserve, have confused language students for years with *How do you do?* – 'How do you do *what*?' an Italian friend of mine often asks herself.

But in my opinion it is the Spanish who have the simplest and most effective way of addressing each other: *Hola. ¿Cómo está?* (Hello, how are you?) 'I'm fine, thanks' is a perfectly adequate response.

LISTENING

1 You are going to hear four people talking about how they were affected by their order of birth. First of all tick (✓) your personal situation.

a   an only child   c   the youngest child

b   the eldest child   d   the middle child

2 Look at the following comments. Which of the people (a to d) do you think is likely to have made them?

1   I always had to look after my brothers and sisters.

2   You don't get spoilt like the youngest or get all your parents' attention like the eldest.

3   I was allowed to do more or less what I liked.

4   I was the centre of attention for my parents which had both positive and negative sides.

3 [🔊] Listen to the speakers and match them with the order of birth in activity 1.

Speaker 1 _____

Speaker 2 _____

Speaker 3 _____

Speaker 4 _____

4 Write down one advantage and one disadvantage of the birth order mentioned by each of the speakers.

_____

_____

_____

_____

_____

_____

_____

WRITING

1 Write a paragraph describing your experience of your birth order and how it affected you.

_____

_____

_____

_____

_____

_____

_____

_____

_____

_____

_____

_____

_____

_____

2 Write a composition with the title *Friendship*.

_____

_____

_____

_____

_____

_____

_____

_____

_____

_____

_____

_____

_____

_____

_____

_____

_____

3 Passion play

VOCABULARY

1 Look at the silhouettes and write sentences saying what sport you think they are practising.

1 _____
2 _____
3 _____
4 _____
5 _____
6 _____

2 Write down words or expressions you can use to talk about these sports.

1 _____
2 _____
3 _____
4 _____
5 _____
6 _____

3 Match a word in Box A with a word in Box B to form a word to do with sport or a phrasal verb.

A	B
give	jumping
half	kick
kick	ball
base	off
free	time
show	up

4 Write sentences with the words.

1 _____
2 _____
3 _____
4 _____
5 _____
6 _____

LISTENING

1 The sentences below come from various sports commentaries. What sports do you think they refer to?

a She misses a putt and finishes 11 under par.

b Coming up to the turn, she is still leading by a head.

c On lap 34, Taggert is leading with the Brazilian, Greg Tomando, close on his tail.

d Jalabert collided with another cyclist and fell.

e They're off and they're safely over the first gate.

2 ▣ Listen to five extracts from sports commentaries. Match the sentences in activity 1 with the extracts. What sport is each commentary about? Did you guess correctly in activity 1?

1 _____ 4 _____
2 _____ 5 _____
3 _____

3 Complete the sentences with information from the commentaries.

1 The Spaniard, Miguel Indurain, has won the race for the last _____.

2 Helen Pierce _____ the competition by one stroke.

3 Taggert wins the race for the _____ time.

4 Chrissie May loses ground at the _____.

5 Jennifer Green on Software had _____ faults in the jump off.

GRAMMAR

1 Complete the sentences by putting the verb in the correct tense. Choose from the verbs below.

win   ask   arrive   lead   choose   applaud   spend watch   play   walk

1   The Chicago Bulls _____ the Philadelphia 76ers in the final tomorrow.

2   Jane loves riding. She (always) _____ us to buy her a horse.

3   When the teams _____ on the field, the respective national anthems are played.

4   The player who _____ the draw usually _____ to serve first.

5   '... and that's it, the whistle's gone, it's half-time and New Zealand _____ twenty-three to six.'

6   Millions of people _____ cricket on the TV in Britain at the weekend.

7   The players _____ onto the court now and the crowd _____ them enthusiastically.

8   Every day she _____ at least three hours training in the gym.

2 Write sentences with *I wish* saying what the people disapprove of.

1   They keep complaining about not having enough money.

   I wish they didn't always complain about not having enough money.

2   He's always playing computer games.

   _____

3   All they do is sit around gossiping about people.

   _____

4   He's always losing money at the races.

   _____

5   She keeps asking me to take her dancing.

   _____

6   I'm always getting lost.

   _____

3 Criticise the following behaviour and habits. You can look back at the *Functions* box in your Student's Book.

1   I eat two bars of chocolate every day.

   _____

2   The children fight from morning till night.

   _____

3   She says she enjoys going to games but I'm sure she doesn't really.

   _____

4   Tennis players who have big serves are very boring to watch.

   _____

5   Alpine skiers queue for ages at ski lifts just to ski for a few minutes.

   _____

SOUNDS

1   [cassette] Listen to the sentences and put a tick (✓) if the speaker sounds disapproving.

1   They're always doing some form of sport.

2   He's always travelling around with the local football team.

3   She keeps asking for time off to go fishing.

4   They're always arguing about their children's education.

5   I keep telling her that it is terribly boring.

6   We keep trying to get him interested in sport.

   [cassette] Listen again and say the sentences aloud.

2   How do you pronounce the words below? Put them in two groups according to the way you pronounce the letter 'u'.

   /ʌ/: _____

   /ɜː/: _____

   current   turn   jump   club   hurdles   fur   under fun   purpose

   [cassette] Listen and check.

The attractive outfits. The sound and smell of horses. There's something magnificent about showjumping. Unfortunately all this splendour is too expensive for most people to contemplate. Luckily, the egalitarian Scandinavians have come up with the answer. For the past ten years, Swedish pet owners have been training their rabbits to jump small obstacles. Now rabbit showjumping has reached the status of a recognised national sport.

Crowds all over Sweden flock to see the highly trained competitors negotiating hurdles closely modelled on actual horse showjumping courses, albeit somewhat scaled down. A rabbit can jump obstacles up to three feet high with appropriate encouragement. The secret is early training: left to their own devices, rabbits tend to head downwards rather than upwards.

Last November, a national body was organised for the new sport and now there are 23 clubs catering for about 4,000 fiercely competitive jumping bunnies. There are also clubs in Denmark and Norway, where last year's championship was won by a buck called Ole Hoiland.

Of course, it will be argued that sending various domestic examples of *Oryctalagus cuniculus* out to do battle before crowds of baying enthusiasts is cruel, but in comparison with what happens to most of their peers this is a veritable rest-cure. At least when they're leaping enthusiastically through the air with a little harness around their necks they're not being treated to an extremely close look at various cosmetics and household cleaning products.

'Jumping rabbits live longer than other rabbits,' confirms Lisbeth Jansson, whose daughter Louise owns the current Swedish national champion. 'And they like jumping: otherwise they wouldn't jump. That's the natural way for a rabbit to move.' Flames of Flame, as he is known, won two gold medals and one silver at last year's championship, bringing his total victories to an impressive 34. He is, apparently, a very popular performer. 'He's the King,' says Mrs Jansson.

The first European rabbit showjumping championships take place in Denmark later this year. It remains to be seen whether the British will be represented. Sadly, it seems unlikely that any of our bunnies will be mounting the winner's rostrum in Denmark. As yet, there seem to be no showjumping rabbits in the country. Still, it's early days and there's still time for an enthusiast to enter the championship, but there is a snag. Win or lose,

your best jumpers would have to stay in quarantine for six months after the event, which would hardly help their training schedule.

You could bring them back into the country: but you'd have to eat them first.

READING

1 Read the passage and answer these questions.

1 What new sport does the passage describe?

2 What other sport is it similar to?

3 What is the main advantage of this sport?

4 Where is the sport developing for the moment?

5 Why can't the British take part in this sport?

2 Answer the questions and try to guess the meanings of the words or phrases.

1 *negotiating hurdles*
   What are the rabbits expected to do on the course?

2 *albeit, somewhat scaled down*
   How big are the jumps?

3 *left to their own devices*
   With or without training?

4 *flock*
   Do a lot of people come to see these competitions?

5 *peers*
   Other rabbits or other species?

6 *snag*
   Would it be easy for British rabbits to take part in competitions abroad?

3 Are these statements true, false or is there no evidence in the passage?

1 Rabbit jumping is not an expensive sport to participate in.

2 Rabbits need training because they don't jump spontaneously.

3 Many rabbits are used to test products to see if they are safe for humans.

4 Jumping rabbits live longer because they are happier.

5 Most people in Scandinavia prefer rabbit jumping to showjumping.

6 Rabbit jumping is becoming popular in Britain.

4 Answer the questions.

1 *... the egalitarian Scandinavians have come up with the answer.*
   The answer to what?

2 *... but in comparison with what happens to most of their peers ...*
   What happens to most of their peers?

3 *... this is a veritable rest-cure.*
   What does *this* refer to?

4 *You could bring them back into the country: but you'd have to eat them first.*
   Who or what does *them* refer to?

5 What is the tone of the passage?

serious   amusing   ironic   matter-of-fact

WRITING

1 How would you train a rabbit to jump? Write a few sentences describing a possible training schedule.

_____

_____

_____

_____

_____

2 Do you agree or disagree with the following statements? Write one or two sentences giving your reasons.

1 Women's tennis is much more boring to watch than men's tennis.

_____

_____

_____

_____

2 The intensive practice of sport can be very harmful to the development of children.

_____

_____

_____

3 Fox hunting and bull fighting are unnecessarily cruel and should be banned.

_____

_____

_____

_____

4 People who participate in individual sports rarely practise team sports.

_____

_____

_____

_____

3 Choose one of the issues in activity 2 and write a short essay presenting the arguments in favour of and those against the view expressed in the statement. Present your own views in the conclusion.

13

VOCABULARY AND READING

1 The reading passage is from a guide to Madrid. Look at the headings (a to h) below and write down four or five words you would expect to find in each section of the guide.

a Live music *concert* _____

b Things to do _____

c Museums _____

d Getting around _____

e Shopping _____

f Cafés, bars, nightclubs _____

g Tourist information _____

h Restaurants _____

2 Look quickly at the passage and match the headings (a to h) in activity 1 with the different sections (1 to 8) of the passage.

3 Where in Madrid could you go if you wanted:

1 a reasonably priced meal?

_____

2 a city tour with a free guide?

_____

3 to see works by Goya?

_____

4 to drink cocktails?

_____

5 to buy unusual souvenirs?

_____

6 to listen to rock music?

_____

7 to see a football match?

_____

8 to see works by modern artists?

_____

4 Imagine you are going to visit Madrid for a long weekend. What will you do and in what order? Write six sentences.

1 First of all, ... _____

2 _____

3 _____

4 _____

5 _____

6 Finally, ..._____

GRAMMAR AND FUNCTIONS

1 The sentences below talk about the future. Put 'P' by the sentences which express a prediction, 'I' by those which express an intention and 'D' by those which express a decision at the moment of speaking.

1 Look at those clouds, it's going to rain.

2 We're going to catch the two o'clock train to Munich.

3 I'll carry your bag if you like.

4 His train arrived at ten so he'll be here any minute.

5 I'll give you a lift into town if you're ready.

6 You'll be late if you don't hurry up.

7 I'm going to buy Peter a present this afternoon.

8 Wait here, I'll be back in a minute.

2 Match the sentence with the function it expresses.

1 I'll come with you if you want.

2 We'll take her to Disneyland for her 10th birthday.

3 Will you post this for me if you're going out?

4 If you don't hurry up you'll miss your flight.

5 No, thank you, I won't join you.

6 I'm sure you'll really enjoy the trip.

7 Will you come with us to the concert?

a a promise

b a refusal

c an offer

d an invitation

e a warning

f a prediction

g a request

14

City Guide

For the visitor, Madrid is one of the most accessible of capitals because everything is upfront. The best times to visit are spring and autumn – but if you can stand the summer heat in August, when the Madrileños are all on holiday, the city feels as if it's yours alone.

1

Public transport in the centre can be slower than walking. A single Metro fare is Pts 125; a day ticket Pts 625. Bus fares cost the same and taxis are among Europe's cheapest.

2

The main office is at Duque de Medinaceli 2 and there is a smaller one on the Plaza Mayor. In both offices you can get free leaflets about the sights to visit and at the main office you can book a city tour with a free bilingual guide. Staff will book concert and theatre tickets and deliver them to your hotel.

3

There are fewer free *tapas* than there used to be, but alcohol and coffee flow as freely as ever. Bars open until very late and range from the expensive and interestingly furnished (the legendary Chicote, a classic for cocktails) to the cheap and interestingly peopled (Candela). Café Gijón is informally elegant, as is Le Cock. A small hours trawl around the Santa Ana district is recommended. You may also like to try the open-air bars along Paseo de la Castellana.

4

Madrid is the focal point for Spain's many regional cuisines. You can try places ranging from Lhardy, where haute cuisine in Madrid was born, to any of the restaurants in the Barrio Popular serving three-course menus for Pts 1,000 or less. Basque, Catalan and Galician palates are also widely catered for.

5

For live concerts there is the Auditorio Nacional de Música. For rock music, there are a number of clubs including the well-known Aqualung and Revolver. If you fancy flamenco, with the chance of ending up dancing yourself, try Al Andalús or Casa Patas.

6

Madrid has 42 museums, most of which are closed on Mondays and in August. If you are neither Spanish nor a student, you usually have to pay. The renowned Prado is rich in works by Velázquez and Goya. For contemporary art, visit the vast Centro de Arte Reina Sofía – it contains Picasso's magnificent *Guernica*.

7

The siesta means shops shut about 13.30 and reopen around 17.00. For knick-knacks, atmosphere and pickpockets, visit the Rastro flea market late on a Sunday morning. The magnificent Gran Vía is an irresistible temptation to spend. The opulent Corte Inglés department stores are open from 10.00 until 21.00.

8

- The royal palace, Palacio Real, has 4,000 rooms.
- Take the Strawberry Train from Atocha station to Aranjuez – a replica of the old trains which used to bring strawberries to the city.
- Watch Real Madrid play. Santiago Bernabeu is one of the world's great football stadiums.
- Make a sunset visit to the startling Templo de Debod. This little piece of ancient Egypt was given to Spain by the Egyptian government.

3 Write a sentence using the future simple for each of the functions (a to g) in activity 2.

1 _____
2 _____
3 _____
4 _____
5 _____
6 _____
7 _____

4 Complete the sentences with a suitable tense. There may be more than one answer. Choose from the verbs below.

get come shut leave remind catch eat
stay visit

1 This evening we _____ at a Spanish restaurant in town.
2 The coach _____ at eleven on Saturdays.
3 I _____ the nine o'clock train to Bratislava.
4 Goodness, it's already nine o'clock, I _____ with you now.
5 If he forgets, (you) _____ him about the meeting?
6 They _____ Rome and Florence on the trip.
7 The shops _____ between twelve and three.
8 I _____ the ten o'clock flight to Chicago.
9 Usually they _____ for at least a fortnight.
10 But this time they _____ for a week.

Dear Mother,
   Today's the big day. We're leaving on the ten o'clock flight from Heathrow and arriving in Madrid at twelve. When we arrive we'll take a taxi to the hotel and get freshened up. Then we'll go out for (1) _____ to get the feel of the city. We haven't made very many definite arrangements because we want to feel free. Peter is going to a (2) _____ on Saturday which he had to book in advance. And I'm going to the (3) _____ on Friday to see Carmen, I had to book that too. I hope we'll find some good places in the evenings where we can (4) _____ and listen to flamenco music. Peter says he wants to have a go at dancing it but I think he's only trying to embarrass me. There's supposed to be a really good flea market on (5) _____ where you can find bargains of all sorts. I thought maybe I could find some unusual (6) _____ there. We're especially looking forward to tasting some of the (7) _____ in the restaurants.
   One place I really want to get to see is the Prado art gallery. There are a lot of very (8) _____ there, including works by Velázquez and Goya. Peter isn't so keen, he's more interested in (9) _____ and wants to go to the Centro de Arte Reina Sofia to see Picasso's Guernica. We'll probably visit the galleries on Monday morning then go for a (10) _____ round the city in the afternoon.
   I'll phone you as soon as I get back home.
   Love from
   Mary

LISTENING

1 🔊 Listen to Mary and Peter discussing what they're going to do during their stay in Madrid. Tick (✓) the things they mention.

1 go to a football match
2 go on a train
3 listen to flamenco music
4 go to the flea market
5 visit the Prado art gallery
6 spend an evening in a cheap bar
7 go to a restaurant and eat a local speciality
8 go to a cocktail bar
9 visit the royal palace
10 have a siesta

2 🔊 Read the postcard from Mary to her mother. Listen again and complete it with a few words.

SOUNDS

🔊 Listen and put a tick (✓) if you hear *'ll* and a cross (x) if you hear *will*.

1 It will be late.
2 When will you get there?
3 What will you do?
4 Where will we stay?
5 It will arrive at twelve.
6 We will stroll along the seafront.
7 What will happen if it rains?
8 Something will happen before you go.

🔊 Listen again and repeat.

WRITING

1 Choose a town that you know well and write down things that are likely to be of interest there for visitors.

_____
_____
_____
_____
_____
_____

2 Imagine you have just arrived on a trip to this town. Write a letter to a friend or relative at home saying what your plans are. You can use the postcard in *Listening* activity 2 as a model.

_____
_____
_____
_____
_____
_____
_____
_____
_____
_____
_____
_____
_____
_____
_____
_____
_____

VOCABULARY

1 Match each word in Box A with a word in Box B.

A	B
first	by
long	hills
stand	class
fast	side
buffet	lane
quay	haul
foot	car

2 Complete these sentences with the new words or expressions formed in activity 1.

1 The railway ran from the Atlantic Ocean to the _____ of the Andes.

2 I always travel _____; it's much more comfortable.

3 _____ flights take a long time and are very tiring.

4 The ship is moored on the _____.

5 If you want a snack you can go to the _____.

6 You overtake in the _____ of a motorway.

7 I haven't got a ticket for the flight but I've been put on _____.

3 Circle the words you can use to talk about climate and underline those you can use to describe geographical features.

frost foothills rainy season deck winter destination tracks heat tropical sea tide sun rhythm moon temperature valley dust halo journey stream freezing

4 Circle the words you can use to describe mood and underline those you can use to describe behaviour.

cruel shy nostalgic miserable kind tense honest content lazy vulgar romantic satisfied discontented reluctant empty optimistic ruthless melancholic

WRITING

Write a few lines describing the climate and geographical features of your country.

_____

_____

_____

_____

READING

1 Read the passage and choose the sentence below which best summarises the content of the article the man read in a magazine.

1 Life starts at thirty.

2 When you reach thirty you should take a long hard look at who you are.

3 Things you should have accomplished by the time you are thirty.

4 At thirty there is still time to change your ways, at forty it is too late.

2 Are these statements about the writer true or false according to the passage?

1 He thinks that magazine articles with amusing lists are only a means of filling space.

2 He enjoys going to operas and watching Eric Rohmer movies.

3 He is relatively satisfied with his life so far.

4 He has travelled extensively.

5 He has changed a great deal over the last 30 years.

3 Find six things the writer mentions to illustrate how lucky he has been in life so far. Write sentences in the present perfect.

He has never broken any bones.

1 _____
2 _____
3 _____
4 _____
5 _____
6 _____

4 Find two things that he has not done and which, according to the magazine, he should have done.

1 _____
2 _____

5 Underline three general characteristics which he attributes to himself.

In this month's issue of GQ magazine there is a list of '101 things you should have done by the time you're 30'. In general I'm suspicious of these 'amusing' lists. I've written enough of them to know that they're usually a lazy way to fill space between adverts. However, I'm going to be 30 next month, so I had to have a look. I discovered to my surprise that I've fulfilled less than half the requirements. Having read the list again I realised that there were some things on it which I wish I'd done. The time has come to take stock of the past 30 years.

I don't want to gloat but I have to tell you that I've been pretty lucky: no bones broken, no major illnesses, both parents still alive, I live somewhere I like. I've had my heart broken enough times to know it hurts but not too many times to need therapy. I dare say I've broken one or two hearts as well so there's a nice balance. Most of my infant pain has now been processed into jokes. I've had a decent enough education not to feel a fool for despising opera or not to think I'm stupid for being bored by the films of Eric Rohmer. I have some good friends, some of whom I've known more than half my life. I like them enough to admit that some of them are cleverer than me, or funnier, or kinder or better looking. So far so good.

It's when I consider the small details of my life that I feel a twinge of disappointment. Lack of travel is an area where I appear to be particularly deficient. I've visited a smattering of European cities, I've been to the States a few times and I once fell asleep on a train and ended up in Cardiff. Try as I might to batter my Globetrotter suitcase, the prospect of inoculations, long-haul flights and hotels without my local TV station has always put me off.

One area where I have failed miserably is car ownership. By the time you are thirty, according to the magazine, you should have a flashy car. For the last three years I have been happily driving around in my mother's old estate car which is anything but flashy.

But it's not all negative. There have been small triumphs and pleasures, of course: I'm proud of some of my writing; I adopted a dog who was miserable and is happy now; and about five years ago I made a decision to stop wasting my life by trying to be liked. The consequences of that last decision are most interesting … I'm not liked. But I like that.

All in all, I've bumbled along for 30 years methodically collecting minor experience. I don't throw things away, I don't forget things and I don't make a lot of noise. I like the same things now that I did 15 years ago – books, art, films, friends, women, football, food. And when I look at photographs of myself as a child I find a pleasing continuity.

GRAMMAR

1 Rewrite these sentences using the present perfect continuous where it is possible.

1 For the last three years I have happily driven around in my mother's old estate car.

For the last three years I have been happily driving around in my mother's old estate car.

2 I've bumbled along for 30 years methodically collecting minor experience.

3 I am proud of a number of articles I've written.

4 I haven't travelled enough in the last few years.

5 I have lived with my adopted dog for five years now.

6 She has written books all her adult life.

7 She has known her second husband since 1990.

8 They have lived in South America since 1990.

2 Write down five things which you are particularly pleased to have done in the last ten years. Use the present perfect.

1 _____
2 _____
3 _____
4 _____
5 _____

3 Are there things which you have not done yet and which you would like to do? Write a few sentences.

4 Look at these pairs of sentences and explain the choice of tense in each case. You may wish to look back at the *Grammar* box in your Student's Book.

1 a They've travelled four hundred kilometres today.

b They've been travelling all day.

2 a He has been staying in New York.

b He has stayed in New York.

3 a He has been training hard this afternoon.

b He has trained hard this afternoon.

4 a They've slept all day.

b They've been sleeping all day.

5 a She's bought a lot of presents for friends this week.

b She's been buying presents for friends all this week.

SOUNDS

1 🔲 Listen to these compound words and underline the final consonants in the first parts of the compound words which you hear.

first class   long-haul   stand-by   fast lane   buffet car   opening hours   second class   cross-channel

🔲 Listen and repeat.

2 Circle the word with a different vowel sound.
1 cargo   sharp   embark   bizarre   fare   starvation
2 sand   haze   halo   radio   pace   aimless
3 lull   full   dust   sun   hum   study
4 stranger   sugar   author   prefer   writer   Venezuela
5 swollen   bloated   coconut   horizon   evoke   roast

🔲 Listen and check.

LISTENING

1 You are going to hear five people talking about how they feel when watching the sun set. Look back at the list of words in *Vocabulary* activity 4 and decide which words you would use to describe your feelings.

2 🔲 Listen and match the speakers with their thoughts.

Speaker 1 ☐   Speaker 4 ☐
Speaker 2 ☐   Speaker 5 ☐
Speaker 3 ☐

a 'I can't help thinking that another day is gone and I haven't done a lot yet.'
b 'I remember the past.'
c 'I think of the inexorability of things.'
d 'It makes me feel very small and insignificant.'
e 'I think about the future.'

3 🔲 Listen again and write down the words or expressions the speakers use to describe their mood.

Speaker 1 _____
Speaker 2 _____
Speaker 3 _____
Speaker 4 _____
Speaker 5 _____

WRITING

1 Would you say that in general you have been lucky in life so far? What characteristics would you attribute to yourself today? Would you say you have changed a lot? Write a short passage about yourself.

_____
_____
_____
_____
_____

2 Write a few lines describing your mood in the following situations. Try to use some of the words in *Vocabulary* activity 4.

travelling alone in a train   contemplating a beautiful sunset   stuck in a traffic jam

_____
_____
_____
_____
_____

VOCABULARY

1 Find twenty-two words you can use to talk about medical matters in the puzzle below.

P	R	E	S	C	R	I	P	T	I	O	N
A	W	O	U	N	D	B	L	O	O	D	I
I	A	I	H	E	A	R	T	C	U	T	N
N	R	N	C	H	E	M	I	S	T	A	T
P	D	T	A	C	L	I	N	I	C	B	E
A	T	M	C	O	N	S	U	L	T	L	N
T	O	E	S	I	C	K	O	L	Y	E	S
I	I	N	J	E	C	T	I	O	N	T	I
E	Z	T	D	I	S	E	A	S	E	S	V
N	I	N	J	U	R	Y	N	U	R	S	E
T	E	M	P	E	R	A	T	U	R	E	X
A	M	B	U	L	A	N	C	E	Z	B	A

2 Complete the passage with words from the puzzle.

The night _____ gave him a _____ killer, took his _____ pressure and _____ and started to dress the _____ on his leg. The _____ had arrived by _____ the previous evening after being involved in a car crash on the motorway. He had a severe head _____ and a broken leg. He was still in the _____ care unit but would no doubt be operated on later in the day.

Another patient had been admitted during the night with a _____ attack. She too was in _____ care at the moment, and if her condition improved would be transferred to the main _____ in a few days.

Out-patients was particularly busy this morning. The _____ on duty had been working non-stop since eight and at midday there were still about ten people in the waiting room. She had seen one small boy who was so _____ he

had been immediately admitted to hospital. But the majority of people who came to out-patients went away with _____.

3 Complete the chart with the corresponding verbs.

Noun	Verb
lie	_____
deception	_____
report	_____
humour	_____
consultation	_____
appointment	_____
prescription	_____
apology	_____
application	_____

READING

1 Read the short story *The Anniversary* and find out what anniversary it refers to.

2 Put these events in the order in which they happened.
a He met a gorgeous lady in the Tuileries gardens.
b He had a meal and took a bath.
c He took a train to Paris.
d He married Sandra in London.
e He took the Metro to the Tuileries.
f He watched a young couple walking hand in hand in the Tuileries gardens.
g He found a note from his wife.
h He went to the Tuileries for his lunch break.

The Anniversary

I took a sip from the cappuccino and relaxed in my first-class Eurostar seat as the train sped through the French countryside en route to Paris. I wasn't even sure why I was on the train in the first place. It certainly wasn't like me to drop everything and shoot off to somewhere like Paris. You see, as my wife Sandra keeps telling me, I've become boring in my old age. But then, I suppose Sandra was the reason I was heading for the French capital.

When I came home from work the night before, I'd found one of her notes on the kitchen table. It simply said that she needed to get away for a few days and would be back later in the week. I wasn't particularly worried. She'd done this several times during our 22 years of marriage but she always came back when she was ready. We had been having a few problems recently and I had to admit that our relationship had gone a bit stale since our youngest daughter had left for university.

After throwing Sandra's note in the bin, I searched the fridge for something to eat. When I'd finished the meal, I undressed and got into the bath. As I was relaxing in the bath, it dawned on me that the following day it would be 25 years exactly since Sandra and I first met in Paris. We had always celebrated this date together – but this time she'd obviously decided to spend it away from me. I couldn't blame her really. I'd been working long hours lately and we barely saw each other.

Lying there in the bath, I suddenly felt compelled to return to Paris on the twenty-fifth anniversary of our first meeting. Maybe it would do me good. I decided right then to catch the first Eurostar train in the morning.

Eventually the train glided into the Gare du Nord in Paris. I got off and wandered across the concourse; I didn't really know where I was heading for, so I bought a ticket and descended an escalator into the Metro. I got on a train and found a seat and stared out of the window.

As the train rattled its way along, I found my mind wandering back to that day, 25 years ago. I'd been working in a merchant bank in Paris. I remember it being a wonderful spring day and I'd decided to spend my lunch break in the Tuileries gardens. I had sat down on a bench to eat my baguette and salami when this gorgeous young lady came up and asked if she could join me. She had a bottle of white wine and some fruit. We shared our lunch and chatted for ages. Her name was Sandra and she was working in Paris as a nanny. We married three years later back in London.

When I eventually emerged from the Metro I discovered I was within walking distance of the Tuileries. I decided to see if I could find the bench where we first met, and as it was almost midday, I bought a baguette and some salami and headed for the gardens. The bench was still in the same place as it had been all those years ago. It was empty, so I wandered over and sat down. I took the baguette and salami out of the bag and put them on my lap.

I watched as a young couple walked hand in hand through the gardens, both obviously in love. What had happened to that young couple who'd sat on this same bench a quarter of a century ago? Surely all that love couldn't have just disappeared? I sat back and closed my eyes, lost in thought.

Suddenly, …

3 **Correct the following statements.**

1 Sandra left a note telling her husband she was going to Paris for a few days.

_____

2 He was uneasy because his wife never went away on her own.

_____

3 Their relationship had improved since their daughter had left home.

_____

4 He decided to take his wife to Paris for their anniversary.

_____

5 He married his wife in Paris.

_____

4 Can you guess how the story ends. Write a final paragraph for the story.

Suddenly ...

_____

_____

_____

_____

_____

_____

Turn to page 91 and read the end of the story.

SOUNDS

1 🔊 All these words contain the sound /dʒ/. Listen and say the words aloud.

surgeon   injury   injection   emergency   urgent
bandage   badge   apologise   journalist   gorgeous
fridge   majority   management   marriage

2 Underline the /k/ sounds and circle the /tʃ/ sounds in the words below.

psychiatry   wheelchair   crutches   mechanic
teacher   bench   watch   chemist   temperature

🔊 Listen and check.

GRAMMAR

1 Look back at the short story and find an example of each of the following past tenses.

1   past simple

_____

2   past continuous

_____

3   present perfect

_____

4   past perfect

_____

5   past perfect continuous

_____

2 Complete the sentences using the words in brackets.

1   When he first met his wife, ... (bank/Paris)
   he was working in a bank in Paris.

2   As he was relaxing in the bath, ... (return/Paris)
   _____

3   While he was sitting on the bench, ...
   (a lady/ask)
   _____

4   When he had finished his meal, ... (have/bath)
   _____

5   When he emerged from the Metro, ...
   (walk/Tuileries)
   _____

6   As he was sitting in the underground train, ...
   (remember/25 years ago)
   _____

7   He wasn't worried when he found his wife's
   note because ... (several times/marriage)
   _____

8   They saw very little of each other because ...
   (work/long hours)
   _____

9   Before going into the gardens, ... (buy/lunch)
   _____

10 After getting off the train, ... (take/Metro)
   _____

3 Complete the sentences with a change of plan.

1   I was going to apply for a new job but ...
   _____

2   I had hoped to meet ...
   _____

3   I was thinking of going out when ...
   _____

4   I had thought of phoning ...
   _____

5   I was going to ...
   _____

LISTENING

1 🔊 Listen to descriptions of four people. Put the number of the description by the picture. There are two extra pictures.

2 Write down words and expressions the speakers use to describe:

hair styles _____

body size _____

READING AND WRITING

1 Write descriptions for the two remaining pictures in *Listening* activity 1.

_____
_____
_____
_____
_____
_____
_____
_____
_____
_____
_____

2 Read the description of an old sailor and underline verbs in the past perfect simple and circle those in the past perfect continuous.

He was seventy-five when I met him for the first time. He had come to Brazil when he was a young man as a sailor on a merchant ship and he had never gone home again. Since then he had done many things. For many years he had worked as the skipper of a ferry. He had been married three times and had had a number of children. He lived alone except for a servant who had been working for him since he arrived in the country and with whom he quarrelled incessantly. But they were old friends, old men both of them, and they would remain together till death parted them. When I met him he had been running a taxi service for nearly six years and was as lively and happy as he had been all his life.

Write a paragraph similar to the one about the sailor describing the life of an elderly person in your family. Try to use the past perfect simple and continuous.

_____
_____
_____
_____
_____
_____
_____
_____

VOCABULARY

1 Write down words or phrases which you can use to talk about the following landscapes.

mountain

_____

country

_____

desert

_____

seaside

_____

2 Underline the opinion adjectives in the list below.

alpine   breathtaking   dense   dramatic   exotic   lush   monotonous   perfect   picturesque   sinuous   spectacular   steep   stunning   towering   unspoilt

3 Choose five opinion adjectives from the list and write a sentence describing a view you associate with each one.

1 _____

2 _____

3 _____

4 _____

5 _____

SOUNDS

1 Circle the word with a different vowel sound.

1 further   fertile   heard   rugged   curves
2 winding   island   life   river   tiny
3 mountain   south   courteous   mouth   trout
4 peak   feature   deer   meadow   stream
5 brow   low   meadow   plateau   coast

[cassette] Listen and check.

2 Underline the stressed syllables.

oasis   volcano   peninsula   earthquake   cathedral   fertile   waterfall   monotonous   geography   scenery   dramatic   surrounded   paradise

[cassette] Listen and say the words aloud.

3 [cassette] Listen and repeat the phrases below. Notice how the underlined consonants are said together as one sound.

unspoilt town   wooded district   steep part   perfect picture   dramatic country   exotic climate   monotonous scenery   cliff face   dirt track   seaside town

READING

1 The four passages are descriptions of places. Look quickly at the passages and find out what each one describes. Choose from the following:

a village   a town   mountains   a region   cultivated land   a farmhouse

2 Read the passages and decide which contain information about:

a   population
b   human activities
c   climate
d   coastline
e   a river valley
f   the writer's viewpoint
g   mountain scenery
h   time of day

3 Underline words and expressions which reveal the writers' opinions.

4 Where do the passages come from?

A   A novel
B   A travel brochure
C   A guide book
D   An advertisement

1 Patagonia makes up a quarter of Argentina's land area, yet contains only a minor percentage of the population. It is an arid land with only a few centimetres of moisture falling each year, mostly as snow in the winter. For the most part, the climate is moderate. Patagonia offers some of the most monotonous scenery in Latin America, but also some of the most spectacular. The Moreno Glacier stretches 1km across a lake and stands 50m high. The coastline of Chilean Patagonia is a wild and beautiful area with a wide variety of marine wildlife. It's a land of virtually unspoilt mountains, glaciers, lakes and forests, with many national parks, including the spectacular Torres del Paine park.

2 Although I was clearly climbing high up into the mountains, the woods all around were so dense that I had no views. But at the summit the trees parted like curtains to provide a spectacular outlook over the valley on the other side. It was like coming over the top of the earth, like the view from an aeroplane. Steep green wooded hills with alpine meadows clinging to their sides stretched away as far as the eye could see until at last they were consumed by a distant and colourful sunset. Before me a sinuous road led steeply down to a valley of rolling farms spread out along a lazy river. It was as perfect a setting as I had ever seen. And the thing was, every house along the road was a shack. This was the heart of Appalachia, the most notoriously impoverished region of America, and it was just inexpressibly beautiful.

3 High on a sandstone cliff, overlooking a large loop in the beautiful River Wye, is the historic market town Ross-on-Wye. It is a most attractive, friendly town with Tudor timbered houses clustered around the striking 17th-century Market Hall. Dominating any view of Ross-on-Wye is the steep spire of St Mary's Church which reflects elegantly in the waters of the Wye and is especially attractive at night when illuminated against the dark sky. Beside the church are Prospect Gardens from where there is a stunning viewpoint looking down upon the river and out across the surrounding fields and countryside.

4 It was set above the country road that runs between the two medieval hill villages of Menerbes and Bonnieux, at the end of a dirt track through cherry trees and vines. It was a farmhouse, built from local stone which two hundred years of wind and sun had weathered to a colour somewhere between pale honey and pale grey. Everything about it was solid. The spiral staircase which rose from the wine cellar to the top floor was cut from massive slabs of stone. The walls, some of them a metre thick, were built to keep out the winds of the Mistral. Attached to the back of the house was an enclosed courtyard, and beyond that a bleached white stone swimming pool. In the afternoon sun, with the wooden shutters half-closed like sleepy eyelids, it was irresistible.

GRAMMAR

1 The words below are all nouns. Some of them can be used as adjectives before another noun. Make as many combinations as possible.

agriculture bed bridge centre cliff climate coast country desert garden hill island journey land market mountain mouth pasture path peak plane pond river road seaside south surface town valley vegetation walk

mountain agriculture
river bed
_____
_____

2 Look back at the passages and find five adjectival phrases using *with*.

_____
_____
_____
_____
_____

3 Put the adjectives in the correct order and choose a suitable noun from the list below.

hills valley castles coastline roads plains peninsula island villa

1 steep beautiful wooded
_____

2 ruined stone romantic
_____

3 single-track spectacular winding
_____

4 vast windswept dry
_____

5 marble two-storey elegant
_____

4 Write similar phrases with two or three suitable adjectives for the remaining words in the list in activity 3.

1 _____
2 _____
3 _____
4 _____

5 Rewrite these sentences to form one sentence.

1 The region is wild. It is exceptionally beautiful. There is a vast national park.
_____

2 There is a spectacular glacier. It is fifty metres high.
_____

3 The streets are lined with 19th-century buildings. They are elegant. They have six storeys.
_____

4 The road is steep. It is sinuous. It has shacks along one side.
_____

5 The hills are steep. They are covered with woods. There are sheep grazing on the lower slopes.
_____

6 Look back at the reading passages and underline words and phrases used to describe position.

LISTENING

1 🔲 Listen to three people talking about a view they particularly like. What is the view of? Where is it from?

View 1 _____

View 2 _____

View 3 _____

2 Write down the words or phrases they use to describe their opinions.

Speaker 1 _____

Speaker 2 _____

Speaker 3 _____

3 Look at these incomplete extracts from the listening passage. Decide which description they come from. Put the number of the speaker by the extract.

a Although it was summer, some of the higher peaks were _____ . ☐

b There was an extraordinary sense of ordered beauty as if the whole scene was an _____ . ☐

c Then _____ the clouds were the magnificent mountains. ☐

d ... when we reached the _____ there was a wonderful view of the paddy fields. ☐

e Above the sea was a narrow strip of land but we were _____ to make out any details. ☐

f ... and I could see rivers gently _____ through the valleys. ☐

4 📼 Listen again and complete the extracts by writing a few words in the spaces.

WRITING

Look at the pictures and write short descriptions for each one.

Strange sensations

VOCABULARY

1 Complete the sentences with a suitable verb of perception from the list below. You may be able to use more than one verb. You may have to change the form of the verb.

hear   see   feel   watch   listen to   notice

1   They were _____ a programme on TV so they didn't _____ their baby coughing.

2   From where she stood she couldn't _____ the snake clearly but she could _____ it hissing.

3   I _____ someone slap me on the back. I turned around and _____ my old friend standing smiling.

4   He was _____ the radio when he _____ the car going past the house.

5   She lay awake _____ her husband snoring. He really was impossible!

6   I could _____ my father whistling in the next room.

7   As we walked up the lane, we _____ a light flashing near the old barn.

8   I could _____ them laughing in the next room.

2 Circle the odd-one-out. Write a few words explaining your choice.

1 pat	stroke	slap	groan	tap
2 stare	sour	glance	gaze	glimpse
3 creak	squeeze	grab	grasp	hold
4 sob	sigh	whisper	bark	laugh
5 bitter	sweet	scented	salty	tasty

3 Write sentences using the odd words in activity 2.

1   _____

2   _____

3   _____

4   _____

5   _____

READING

1 Read the first part of *The Thing That Went Scratch in the Night* and answer these questions.

1   How many people are mentioned and who are they?

2   Who is Granta?

3   Which two senses predominate in the story?

2 Decide where these participle clauses go in the gaps (1 to 5) in the story.

a   Panting from time to time because of the heat, ...

b   Pulling the dog aside, ...

c   Recognising her name, ...

d   Jumping off the bed, ...

e   ... carrying the chicken salad and a glass of cool white wine, ...

3 Decide if these sentences are true or false.

1   The man had supper then went to his bedroom.

2   He let the dog lie on the bed next to him even though it was very hot.

3   He was relieved to be alone for the evening.

4   He heard someone approaching the house.

5   The dog barked because it could sense something in the room.

6   The man decided to go home because it was too hot in the house.

7   The young couple didn't believe his story.

4 Answer these questions.

1   Find four words for different noises a dog makes.

2   Underline the words and phrases in the story which convey fear.

3   Find verbs which mean: a) take something roughly; b) touch kindly with the hand; c) push away.

4   Which verb is the odd-one-out: a) beat; b) thump; c) hammer; d) strike; e) scratch?

5   Which two words mean to jump: a) stretch; b) leap; c) bound; d) rise?

The Thing That Went Scratch in the Night

'Sure you'll be all right? We'll be back in the morning.' His son sounded anxious.

'If you're going for God's sake go!' exclaimed his father impatiently. 'I'm fine, I'm just feeling tired. I'll have my dinner and go to bed. There's a play I want to listen to on the radio.'

'Your plate's in the fridge,' said his daughter-in-law, as if she was speaking to a child, 'a nice cold chicken and salad. Granta's bowl is beside it.'

'Good,' he said, 'Granta will look after me, won't you?'

1 ☐ the gentle, light honey Labrador thumped her tail with pleasure.

'Now off you go and enjoy yourselves.'

He was relieved when he heard the car driving off. He gave Granta her meal and

2 ☐ went to his bedroom. He undressed and stretched out on his bed.

3 ☐ Granta stretched out beside him. The warmth of her body, folded against his own, was uncomfortable, but there she was, protecting him faithfully and he did not have the heart to shove her away.

He was absorbed in the play when he sensed, suddenly, that the dog was alert – tense. He listened in case there was someone outside, approaching the house. Nothing.

4 ☐ she bounded towards a far corner of the room, whining. Then she barked, a furious, warning bark of alarm.

'What is it?' he called out to her, but he could see nothing.

She leapt back on the bed. He could feel her trembling with fear as he stroked her, the hairs stiff, the hackles risen. 'What is it?' She jumped off again. She barked. She howled.

It was such an agonised sound that it made him shiver.

'What's the matter with you?' And he did hear something, or at least he thought he did, a sort of ... he had no idea what it could be and he could see nothing.

In the next moment her howls ceased. She growled instead at the thing in the corner, preparing to attack whatever was there, or was not there.

Infected now by her panic, anxious to calm her too, he got out of bed and grabbed his stick. A furious din as if she was fighting something – 'Stop it, Granta!' he cried, 'there's nothing there.'

5 ☐ he hammered down blows on the invisible thing in the corner. She seemed reassured, at least she was quiet, but when they were lying on the bed again he could feel her heart beating. Neither of them slept well that night.

The next morning when his son returned he announced he was going home. 'I know it's daft,' he said, in answer to their questions, 'but I think this hideous place is haunted. I wouldn't spend another night in that room for anything. Anyway it's too damned hot.' He was ashamed to mention he had struck at something in the corner that wasn't there, but he told them about Granta – 'and at one moment I was sure I heard, well it's hard to describe, but it was like the noise of someone writing something in pencil, on wood, a scratching sound.'

The young man and woman looked at each other, with private smiles.

31

5 Decide who experienced these feelings and in what circumstances. Write a sentence for each one.

anxious amused uncomfortable impatient frightened ashamed relieved

The son was anxious because he was leaving his father alone for the evening.

_____

_____

_____

_____

_____

_____

_____

_____

_____

_____

_____

_____

GRAMMAR

1 Rewrite these sentences as participle clauses.

1 When they were lying on the bed again he could feel her heart beating.
Lying on the bed again, he could feel her heart beating.

2 They smiled at each other and walked away.

_____

3 He got out of bed and grabbed his stick.

_____

4 She growled at the thing in the corner and prepared to attack.

_____

5 Because he found the door open, he went in.

_____

6 She came downstairs and saw the car drive off.

_____

7 As I crossed the road I noticed him walk into a shop.

_____

8 She saw it was raining so she took an umbrella.

_____

2 Rewrite the relative clauses as participle clauses.

1 The young woman who works at my office invited me out to lunch.
The young woman working at my office invited me out to lunch.

2 Tourists who go to Italy in the spring are very sensible.

_____

3 Foreigners who visit the city usually stay in the centre.

_____

4 The man who is walking towards us comes from the university.

_____

5 People who live in that part of town are very lucky.

_____

6 The family who live next door have just moved in.

_____

_____

3 Complete the sentences with a suitable verb from the list below in its infinitive or -*ing* form.

grab scratch groan sigh whisper hit

1 He could hear something _____ in the corner of the room.

2 I felt someone _____ me on the head. I woke up in hospital.

3 I could hear the children _____ but I couldn't make out what they were saying.

4 I saw the man _____ the handbag then he disappeared.

5 I heard him _____ when he took the tax form out of the envelope.

6 Then I heard him _____ with relief when he saw the small amount he had to pay.

LISTENING

1 ▣ Listen to the next part of *The Thing That Went Scratch in the Night* and find out what the noise the old man heard in the bedroom really was.

2 ▣ Listen again. Complete these sentences with a few words.

1 The young woman regrets _____
_____.

2 The son is surprised that his father believes in ghosts _____
_____.

3 The old man has gone home by _____
_____.

4 When they go into the bedroom, they are surprised to see that the bed _____
_____.

5 The young woman screams because
_____
_____.

6 They find a gap in the floorboards where
_____
_____.

7 The young woman feels ashamed because
_____
_____.

8 They decide not to tell the old man about the snake because _____
_____.

3 Can you guess why the old man didn't know what the 'thing' in the corner was?

4 Read the end of the story and see if you guessed correctly.

A t that moment the old man was back in his village looking forward to the welcome familiarity of his local pub. No 'things' lurked in corners there. As they waited to cross the road, Granta looked up at him with an expression of absolute sympathy.

She had defended him; he had defended her. No cars in sight – so she led the blind man forward and they went into the pub together.

SOUNDS

1 ▣ Here are some words with two or more consonants together. Listen and repeat them.

stroked grasped glimpse strike scratch
stretched thumped grabbed

2 Put the words below into two groups according to how you pronounce the letters 'gh'.

silent _____
_____

/f/ _____
_____

roughly sighed laugh tough frightened
though cough thought taught eighty
enough

▣ Listen and check. Say the words aloud.

WRITING

Look at the list of feelings in *Reading* activity 5. Choose three feelings and for each one write about a situation when you experienced the feeling.

1
_____
_____
_____
_____

2
_____
_____
_____
_____

3
_____
_____
_____
_____

VOCABULARY

1 Put the words below into three groups of your own choice. Use a dictionary to check the meaning of words you don't know.

knock play smile tug grin pat rehearse wave pull laugh cry improvise lines entrance script scream sulk shake hit frown

2 Write sentences with the verbs in brackets. Use the nouns in the list below.

donkey door rope hands goodbye ball

1 (knock)

_____

2 (tug)

_____

3 (hit)

_____

4 (pat)

_____

5 (wave)

_____

6 (shake)

_____

SOUNDS

Listen and repeat the phrases below. Notice how the underlined consonants are said together as one sound.

use<u>d t</u>o go wen<u>t t</u>o school knocke<u>d d</u>own bi<u>g c</u>lassroom happene<u>d t</u>o me too<u>k c</u>are of I'<u>ve f</u>ound them a chea<u>p p</u>lace a wonderfu<u>l l</u>ady ro<u>de t</u>o school bi<u>g g</u>arden

LISTENING

1 Listen to three different descriptions of early school memories. What are the memories about? Are the memories happy or unhappy?

Speaker 1 _____

_____

Speaker 2 _____

_____

Speaker 3 _____

_____

2 Listen to the passages again and note down three memories for each speaker.

Speaker 1 *screaming at top of stairs*

_____

_____

Speaker 2 _____

_____

_____

Speaker 3 _____

_____

_____

READING

1 The passage on page 35 is an extract from *Boy – Tales of Childhood* by Roald Dahl. In it, the writer describes his first memories of kindergarten. Look quickly at the passage and find out if the writer remembers a lot or very little about kindergarten.

2 Read the passage and underline the verbs and expressions he uses to talk about what he remembers.

3 Read the passage again and find:

1 two things he can't remember.

_____

_____

2 two things he can only vaguely remember.

_____

_____

3 two things he remembers well.

_____

_____

Boy – Tales of Childhood

It is astonishing how little one remembers about one's life before the age of seven or eight. I can tell you all sorts of things that happened to me from eight onwards, but only very few before that. I went for a whole year to Elmtree House but I cannot even remember what my classroom looked like. Nor can I picture the faces of Mrs Corfield and Miss Tucker, the two sisters who ran the kindergarten, although I am sure they were sweet and smiling. I do vaguely remember sitting on the stairs and trying over and over again to tie one of my shoelaces, and I have a blurred memory of being made to eat soggy cabbage and greasy sausages at lunchtime, but that is all that comes back to me at this distance of the school itself.

On the other hand, I can remember very clearly the journeys I made to and from the school because they were so tremendously exciting. Great excitement is probably the only thing that really interests a six-year-old boy and it sticks in his mind. In my case, the excitement centred around my new tricycle. I rode to school on it every day with my eldest sister riding on hers. No grown-ups came with us, and I can remember oh so vividly how the two of us used to go racing at enormous tricycle speeds down the middle of the road and then, most glorious of all, when we came to a corner, we would lean to one side and take it on two wheels.

So much, then, for my memories of kindergarten sixty-two years ago. It's not much, but it's all there is left.

GRAMMAR

1 Look at the memories you noted for Speaker 1 in *Listening* activity 2 and write sentences using *remember* + *-ing*.

I remember screaming at the top of the stairs.

1 _____

_____

2 _____

_____

3 _____

_____

2 Look at the memories you noted for Speaker 2 in *Listening* activity 2 and write sentences using *remember* + noun.

_____

1 _____

_____

2 _____

_____

3 _____

_____

3 Look at the memories you noted for Speaker 3 in *Listening* activity 2 and write sentences using *remember* + noun or pronoun subject.

I remember the headmistress accusing me of stealing.

1 _____

_____

2 _____

_____

3 _____

_____

READING

1 Read another extract from Roald Dahl's book and answer these questions.

1 Who was Corkers?

2 What subject did he use to teach?

3 Did the boys like him?

4 Was he a good teacher?

5 Did he use to dress smartly?

2 Underline the words and expressions which describe Corker's appearance and personality.

3 Answer the questions and try to guess the meanings of the words or phrases.

1 *lumbering into*   Did he move
   a) gracefully or b) clumsily?

2 *glare at*   Is this
   a) a friendly or
   b) an unfriendly way of looking at someone?

3 *fish*   Does this mean
   a) take out or b) look for?

4 *crumpled*   Was the paper
   a) folded carefully or b) screwed up in a ball?

5 *dreariest*   Is mathematics
   a) boring or b) interesting?

4 Which words would you use to describe the tone of the passage?

serious gloomy amusing ironic matter-of-fact
lighthearted dreary

There used to be about thirty or more masters at Repton and most of them were amazingly dull and totally colourless and completely uninterested in boys. But Corkers, an eccentric old bachelor, was neither dull nor colourless. Corkers was a charmer, a vast ungainly man with drooping bloodhound cheeks and filthy clothes. He used to wear creaseless flannel trousers and a brown tweed jacket with patches all over it and bits of dried food on the lapels. He was meant to teach us mathematics, but in truth he taught us nothing at all and that was the way he meant it to be. His lessons used to consist of an endless series of distractions all invented by him so that the subject of mathematics would never have to be discussed. He would come lumbering into the classroom and sit down at his desk and glare at the class. We would wait expectantly, wondering what was coming next.

'Let's have a look at the crossword puzzle in today's *Times*,' he would say, fishing a crumpled newspaper out of his jacket pocket. 'That'll be a lot more fun than fiddling around with figures. I hate figures. Figures are perhaps the dreariest things on this earth.'

'Then why do you teach mathematics, sir?' somebody asked him.

'I don't,' he said, smiling slyly. 'I only pretend to teach it.'

Corkers would proceed to draw the framework of the crossword on the blackboard and we would all spend the rest of the lesson trying to solve it while he read out the clues. We enjoyed that.

GRAMMAR

1 Underline all the sentences in the passage on page 36 with *used to*. Whenever it is possible, rewrite the sentences using *would* + infinitive.

_____
_____
_____
_____
_____
_____

2 Find four sentences in the passage with *would* + infinitive. Rewrite the sentences using *used to*.

_____
_____
_____
_____
_____
_____
_____
_____

3 Complete the sentences with *be used to* + noun/*-ing* or *get used to*.

1 I _____ travelling alone so I was very worried before the trip.

2 He _____ eating spicy food so he lost a lot of weight during the trip.

3 When he got a job in India he had to _____ eating spicy food.

4 I _____ working such long hours so I was exhausted for the first few days but I soon _____ the long hours.

5 She _____ doing sport so she ached all over after the mountain hike.

6 I had to _____ travelling abroad when I got this job with a foreign company.

7 It took him a long time to _____ his new school.

8 I _____ living in a cold climate and I don't think I will ever _____ it.

4 Write four sentences describing things which you are not used to doing.

I'm not used to cooking my own meals.

1 _____
  _____
2 _____
  _____
3 _____
  _____
4 _____
  _____

5 Write four sentences describing things that you will have to get used to doing in the future.

I'll have to get used to getting up early when I get a job.

1 _____
  _____
2 _____
  _____
3 _____
  _____
4 _____
  _____

WRITING

1 Write a few lines describing your early memories of school. Try to use the following expressions.

I can picture   I remember   sticks in the mind   to have a blurred/clear memory of

_____
_____
_____

2 Write a few lines describing a teacher you remember. Describe a typical lesson.

_____
_____
_____
_____
_____

10 | Rules of law

VOCABULARY

1 Match the words below with the definitions.

jury prosecution judge defence lawyer
magistrate defendant court

1 The person who decides on a sentence.
2 The person who presents the victim's case.
3 The person who presents the case of the
   person standing trial.
4 The person who stands trial.
5 The people who decide whether the person
   standing trial is guilty or innocent.
6 The place where a trial takes place.
7 The person who presides in a court for minor
   offences.

2 Put these legal procedures in the order in which
they usually take place.

a be convicted of an offence
b be charged with an offence
c be sentenced
d be arrested
e be suspected of an offence
f appeal
g stand trial
h be given bail or go into custody

1 _____
2 _____
3 _____
4 _____
5 _____
6 _____
7 _____
8 _____

3 Complete the news reports below with words
from the list. You may need to modify the
nouns and verbs. You may need to use some
words more than once.

forged sentence prison jury extradite
suspended convict lawyer prosecution charge
appeal guilty fine court innocent case

1 A court _____ the former boss of a first
   division football club to one year in
   _____ and another year _____ for
   rigging a soccer match. The sentence was
   harsher than the six-month term sought by the
   _____. The former football boss is to
   _____ against the sentence.

2 The mayor of a major town was found
   _____ of fraud when he was finally
   brought to _____ last month. He fled the
   country two years ago when an enquiry
   revealed he had been using taxpayers' money
   to finance personal projects. The former mayor
   was _____ from America in January. He
   received a two-year prison _____ and
   was _____ £10,000.

3 A _____ sentenced one of Europe's most
   wanted men to seven months' jail for
   possession of _____ documents. After
   serving the sentence he is likely to be
   _____ to Italy where he had escaped
   from jail after he was _____ of murder in
   1991.

4 A 40-year-old man was found not _____
   of murder by a _____ in Birmingham
   this week. The man had been _____
   with the murder of a neighbour in May 1993
   and had spent over a year behind bars before
   his _____ finally came to court this
   month. The man was overwhelmed with relief
   as he left the _____ with his wife. His
   _____ is making a compensation claim
   for the months he spent in prison.

LISTENING

1 🔲 Listen to three news items about various crimes. Write the number of the news item by the crimes the people are found guilty of. Some people may be guilty of more than one crime.

☐ grievous bodily harm ☐ corruption

☐ conspiracy ☐ libel

☐ harassment

2 🔲 Listen again. What punishment were the people sentenced to? Write the number of the news item by the punishments. There are some extra punishments.

☐ fine ☐ community work

☐ suspended jail sentence

☐ court order to keep the peace

☐ ban ☐ warning

☐ jail sentence

3 For each news item, write a sentence describing exactly what the people did.

1 _____

_____

2 _____

_____

3 _____

_____

SOUNDS

🔲 Listen and repeat the sentences. Notice how the 't' in *shouldn't* is not pronounced.

1 You shouldn't make a fuss.

2 You shouldn't park there.

3 They shouldn't ban speeding.

4 You shouldn't come in late.

5 They shouldn't give him away.

GRAMMAR

1 Tick (✓) the pairs of sentences which have the same meaning.

1 He didn't need to show his identity card.
He didn't have to show his identity card.

2 You shouldn't say anything without a lawyer present.
You don't have to say anything without a lawyer present.

3 She should have obtained a work permit.
She had to obtain a work permit.

4 You mustn't smoke in public places.
You aren't allowed to smoke in public places.

5 He didn't have to give the prisoner bail.
He needn't have given the prisoner bail.

6 You needn't appeal against a sentence.
You don't have to appeal against a sentence.

2 Complete these sentences with *must, have to, have got to* or *should*.

1 We haven't seen the Smiths for over a month. We really _____ give them a ring.

2 I _____ fill my tax form in by the end of February every year.

3 I _____ pay my income tax before the end of this month.

4 I haven't had my car checked for ages. I _____ make an appointment with the garage.

5 You _____ (not) forget to bring a letter explaining why you weren't at school last week.

6 If you want to get there before seven o'clock, you _____ leave now.

7 You _____ wear a car seat belt in Britain.

8 You _____ (not) drive over 50 km per hour in the town.

3 Make sentences using *should have* and *shouldn't have* for the following situations.

1   Convincing forgeries of 50,000-rouble notes turned up in Vologda, 240 miles north of Moscow. The forgers had made one mistake, however: the word 'Russia', appearing prominently at the top of the bill, had a letter missing.

The forgers should have checked
more carefully.
They shouldn't have made a spelling
mistake.

2   Raiders stole some 200 training shoes from a sports shop in Alfreton, Derbyshire. They won't find it easy to sell the shoes as they are all for left feet.

_____
_____
_____
_____

3   Robert Ventham, 22, took his golf clubs with him on a smuggling trip to Gibraltar, with the idea of fooling Customs as to the purpose of his visit. As yet, there are no golf courses on the Rock of Gibraltar. Ventham was arrested on his return for possession of smuggled goods.

_____
_____
_____
_____

4   Edilber Guimaraes, 19, was arrested in Belo Horizonte, Brazil for attempted theft at a glue factory. He had stopped to sniff some of the glue he was stealing, fell over and spilt two cans, sticking himself to the floor. He was found 36 hours later and had to be cut loose by firefighters.

_____
_____
_____
_____

WRITING

Look back at the crimes in *Listening* activity 1. Write sentences saying whether you agree or disagree with the punishment the people were sentenced to. If you disagree, say what sentences should have been given.

_____
_____
_____
_____
_____
_____

READING

1 The words and expressions in the box come from the passage called *Space Law*. The passage mentions the following issues. Write down questions that you expect the passage to answer.

ownership

_____

environment and pollution

_____

space traffic

_____

| satellite   flag   research   legal field   treaty |
| launch   celestial bodies   astronaut   birth |
| lawyer   permit   heritage   market   territory |
| business   nationality   satellite   debris   moon |

2 Read the passage and find out if it answers your questions.

3 Decide if these statements are true, false or if there is no evidence.

1   The moon belongs to the United States because it has its flag there.

2   A baby born in a space station would have no specific nationality.

3   A country doesn't have to return space equipment that accidentally lands on its territory.

SPACE LAW

Where no law has gone before: When astronauts blasted off to explore space, lawyers inevitably followed.

Who owns the moon? Throughout history, planting a flag in unclaimed territory has meant ownership, and the United States has its flag on the moon.

If several countries own a space station, what is the nationality of a baby born in space?

Who is responsible for satellite debris and rocket launching pollution?

Can anyone send anything into space?

As the presence of humans in space increases, so must the body of laws governing their actions there. The space movement seems to be towards international research, development, production and operation, and therefore, joint ownership. Things that are governed by place of occurrence – such as ownership rights, contract signing, how to try criminals, and nationality for birth – will have to be redefined legally. An entire body of law for people growing up, doing business and inventing new things in outer space is going to be needed.

Still only a tiny legal field, space law began in 1958 with the formation of the National Aeronautics and Space Administration in the United States. Between 1967 and 1976, the United Nations drafted five international treaties that state:

- All people have equal access to outer space.
- An astronaut or space equipment that accidentally lands in one country must be returned to the launching country.
- Countries are responsible for what they launch.
- Everything in space must be registered.
- The moon and other celestial bodies are the heritage of and are to be shared by all humankind.

The next decades will likely see the creation of new legal precedents. The US aerospace plane currently under development will zoom across half the globe in less than three hours by travelling through outer space. The space lawyers will have to decide whether its activities come under aviation or space laws.

Perhaps the field's greatest challenge will be deciding how to share the financial benefits of space. Which returns us to the question of lunar ownership. The international treaty drafted by the UN states that 'celestial bodies are the heritage of all humankind'. In other words, we all own the moon. And that's a nice surprise for anyone who's dreamed of owning beachfront property – even if it is next to the Sea of Tranquility.

4 In the future, space laws will be made to deal with environmental problems.

5 Only a few countries are allowed to launch rockets into outer space.

6 No countries are allowed to send dangerous substances into space.

7 Everything that is launched into space must be registered.

4 Read the passage again and answer the questions in the opening paragraphs. Which questions cannot be answered?

_____

_____

_____

_____

WRITING

Write down some laws for outer space. They can be as strange as you like. Think about:

pollution research nuclear waste satellites
weapons rockets

_____

_____

_____

_____

_____

_____

_____

_____

_____

_____

VOCABULARY

1 Can you guess what these objects are? You can look back at your Student's Book.

1 You use them to cut paper or textiles.

2 It's a device for opening tins.

3 You use it to heat or cook food in.

4 It's a garden tool for digging.

5 It's a device for opening wine bottles.

6 It's an tool used to make small holes for screws.

7 You use it to sweep the floor.

8 You use this tool to undo or tighten nuts and bolts.

2 Complete the sentences with verbs from the list below. You may have to change the form of some of the verbs.

swallow   soften   smear   relieve   shelter   creep
tickle   spill   sting

1 If you have a headache, take an aspirin in order to _____ the pain.

2 If you _____ wine on the carpet, put salt on it so that it won't make a stain.

3 If a wasp _____ you, _____ tar on your skin in order to prevent it swelling.

4 In order not to suffer from travel sickness, Galton recommended _____ gunpowder and soapy water.

5 In order to _____ leather boots, he broke a raw egg in them.

6 To make children laugh, you can _____ their feet.

7 In order not to be heard when you come home late, you should _____ into the house.

8 If it rains when I'm in town, I _____ in a shop so that I don't get wet.

READING

1 Read the passage called *Beating Jetlag* and underline all the unpleasant effects of jetlag it mentions.

2 Match the advice with the purpose.

1 Take a number of precautions before flying ☐ a to counter the effects of dehydration.

2 Eat foods containing vitamins A and E ☐ b to avoid feeling unwell.

3 Take exercise ☐ c to build up your immune system.

4 Drink a lot of water ☐ d to offset the effects of reduced air pressure.

5 Drink carrot juice before flying ☐ e to overcome oxygen deficiency.

6 Have light, frequent meals ☐ f to prevent your blood circulation slowing down.

3 Find a word in the box which means the same as:

1 an unpleasant feeling when you lose your sense of balance

2 a physical feeling of not being able to move your body easily

3 take exercise to loosen up your body

4 help and improve

5 counter

6 limit

7 physical condition

8 make worse or more acute

> fainting   limber up   intensify   shape
> exacerbate   dizziness   enhance   stiffness
> offset   restrict   disruption

Beating Jetlag

Recovery from jetlag can take as long as a day for every time zone crossed. So if you're flying east–west for your holiday or on business, it is likely to mean a few days of feeling tired or even unwell.

Jetlag is the disruption of the body's natural cycle and some factors make it worse. The artificial atmosphere inside a plane can affect the body in a number of ways and exacerbate the effects of jetlag. If you deal with these, you will arrive in better shape.

Exercising before flights helps to offset the effects on the body of reduced air pressure, and aerobic exercise afterwards helps to reoxygenate it. Drink plenty of water. About a cupful every hour is needed to counter the effects of dehydration. Children may need more. Drinking carrot juice before flying overcomes oxygen deficiency.

Eat light, frequent meals. Heavy meals slow down the blood circulation, which can lead to dizziness and fainting. For two weeks before you fly, eat plenty of foods containing vitamins A and E; they will build up your immune system and help to keep you fit. Sleep as much as you can before the flight and on it. On board, wear earplugs and eye pads because darkness stimulates secretion of the hormones that enhance sleep.

Avoid alcohol, which restricts the brain's oxygen intake. Like tea and coffee, alcohol increases the dehydration effect of flying. If you need to drink to relax, bear in mind that the cabin environment intensifies the effect of alcohol.

Wear loose, comfortable, warm clothes and limber up during flight. Sitting down for several hours slows down the circulation, leading to stiffness, cramps and dizziness. Re-adjust to local time as soon as you can. Bright light helps the body stay alert, so if you are going somewhere sunny stay outside.

Do not smoke before or during the flight since smoking decreases the blood oxygen level. If you need to calm your nerves, try aromatherapy oils which have a sedative effect. Consult your doctor before flying if you are on medication. The effects of some drugs are strengthened at high altitude and some may produce side effects.

GRAMMAR

1 Look at *Reading* activity 2 and write sentences with *to*, *in order to* or *in order not to*. There may be more than one possibility.

1 *Take a number of precautions before flying in order not to feel unwell.*

2 _____

3 _____

4 _____

5 _____

6 _____

2 Answer the questions using *so that*.

1 Why should you eat food high in vitamins before a long flight?
You should eat food high in vitamins so that your immune system is built up and you keep fit.

2 Why is it a good idea to wear eye pads on board?
_____
_____

3 Why should you avoid drinking alcohol?
_____
_____

4 Why should you wear loose clothes?
_____
_____

5 Why should you get some exercise before the flight?
_____
_____

6 Why is it sensible to consult your doctor before flying if you are on medication?
_____
_____

3 Write four sentences using *so that*.

1 (coffee)

_____

_____

2 (smoking)

_____

_____

3 (bright light)

_____

_____

4 (aromatherapy oils)

_____

_____

WRITING

1 Look at the advice in *Vocabulary* activity 2. Would you do any of these things? If not, write sentences saying what you would do.

_____

_____

_____

_____

_____

_____

_____

_____

2 Write a few lines of advice for the following situations.

Your friend gets bitten by a snake when you are walking in the mountains.

_____

_____

You are at a dinner party and your hostess serves you the one food which makes you sick.

_____

_____

You want to improve your spoken English and increase your vocabulary.

_____

_____

_____

LISTENING

1 🔲 You are going to hear two people talking about gadgets in a mail-order catalogue. Listen and put a tick (✓) by the gadgets which the speakers mention.

a   electronic crossword solver

b   an alarm clock with no face or hands

c   microchip controlled Drinkscentre

d   digital hourglass

e   revolving shoe stand

f   glowing pyjamas

g   a Scrabble Computer

h   a cook and mix microwave

2 Write sentences saying what the gadgets are for.

_____

_____

_____

_____

_____

_____

_____

_____

3 🔲 Listen to the conversation again and complete these sentences with adjectives.

1   You've got to be _____ to spend time inventing a stupid thing like that.

2   It's so _____ and more _____ to prepare drinks yourself.

3   It would be _____ to buy one.

4   It would be really _____ for her to have one.

GRAMMAR

1 Put the adjectives below into columns according to whether you use them to describe people or situations.

careless   clever   easy   essential   generous   important   (un)kind   (un)necessary   rare   stupid   thoughtful   useful   useless

People	Situations

2 Complete these sentences with *of* or *for*.

1   It would be really useful _____ her to have one.

2   It would be easy _____ me to keep an eye on you.

3   It's kind _____ you to invite us for the weekend.

4   It's essential _____ her to get a good grade in her exams.

5   It's very thoughtless _____ him to forget your birthday.

6   It's important _____ her to spend time with her grandchildren.

7   It's generous _____ you to bring them presents.

8   It's careless _____ them to lose the book.

3 Write sentences saying what you think of the gadgets described in *Listening* activity 1. Use clauses of contrast. You can look back in your Student's Book.

Although it's very clever, a Scrabble Computer is a stupid idea.

1   _____

2   _____

3   _____

4   _____

SOUNDS

1 Underline the words which are likely to be stressed in *Grammar* activity 2.

2 🔲 Listen and check your answers to activity 1. Say the sentences aloud.

WRITING

Make a list of a few gadgets which you own. Write a passage describing the gadgets and why you bought them. Discuss their advantages and disadvantages.

_____

_____

_____

_____

_____

_____

_____

_____

_____

_____

_____

_____

_____

_____

_____

VOCABULARY

1 Write down six different methods of cooking. You can look in your Student's Book.

Cooking method	Food
bake	fish, cakes
_____	_____
_____	_____
_____	_____
_____	_____
_____	_____

2 For each method, write down food you would cook in this way. Write your answers in the list above.

3 Complete the crossword.

Across
1 If you like your food hot, you can add this.
3 You do this to vegetables with a knife.
5 Cut into little cubes.
7 You eat this with every meal in many countries.
8 Car engine cooking is safe as long as you wrap the food in three layers of _____.
9 If you don't like fat, don't cook your food like this.
10 They're good for your eyesight and packed with vitamin A.
12 This food is high in protein.
13 Uncooked.
14 Cultured dairy food that is full of calcium.
18 You can cook potatoes like this.
19 Another dairy product.
21 When I'm hungry between meals, I have a quick _____.
22 Nice with afternoon tea.
23 If you stay in a hotel in Britain, you will have this for breakfast.
24 When water boils, it turns to _____.
25 If you are poaching fish, you can _____ it in foil.

Down
2 When I eat fruit in a restaurant, I always _____ it.
3 A measure of the energy in food.
4 A good way to cook fish without fat.
6 A child's favourite especially with a hamburger.
7 Potassium-packed fruit that monkeys love to eat.
11 Cashews, almonds, pecans, etc.
15 When you slice this, it makes you cry.
16 If you use too much oil in your cooking, your food will be _____.
17 A favourite white meat in Kentucky.
18 If you want a really rich flavour, use this to cook with instead of oil.
20 Margarine, butter, oil are sources of this high-calorie nutrient.
21 A meat dish or a way of cooking very slowly.

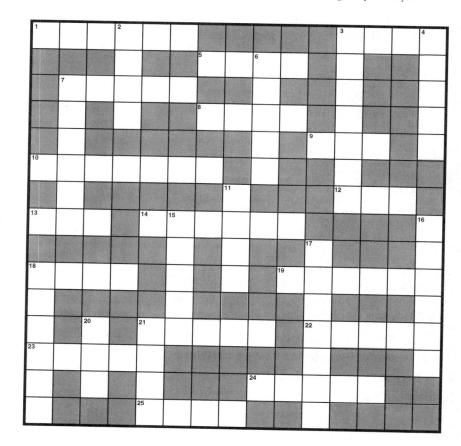

GRAMMAR

1 Put the verb in brackets in the correct tense.

1 If I have time this evening, I (cook) _____ dinner.

2 If I (go) _____ to an Italian restaurant, I always (have) _____ pizza.

3 If he (win) _____ the election next month, he (become) _____ mayor.

4 If I (be) _____ a student again, I (work) _____ harder.

5 If I (have) _____ time, I (cook) _____ dinner more often.

6 If the weather (be) _____ nice tomorrow, we (have) _____ a barbecue.

2 Look back at the list in *Vocabulary* activities 1 and 2. Write sentences with *if* and *when*.

When I bake fish, I cover it with foil. If I baked a cake, I'd fill it with chocolate.

1 _____

_____

2 _____

_____

3 _____

_____

4 _____

_____

5 _____

_____

6 _____

_____

READING

1 Read the passage on page 48 and choose the best title from the list below.

1 Favourite conversation topics

2 The guide to home entertainment

3 How to hold a dinner party

4 Home cooking vs. restaurant food

2 Match the two parts of these sentences.

1 Avoid holding dinner parties in your own home

2 Avoid serious conversation topics

3 You will become a social success

4 There will be embarrassing silences

5 If you go to bed before the end of the meal

6 If you don't hold a dinner party at all

a ... your guests will let themselves out.

b ... as long as you get it right.

c ... if you get it wrong.

d ... you won't risk making a fool of yourself.

e ... unless you are with French people.

f ... unless you're extremely rich and tasteful.

3 Underline five pieces of advice in the passage.

4 Answer the questions and try to guess the meanings of the words or phrases.

1 *a show off* Is this likely to be someone who
   a) likes to attract attention or
   b) keeps to himself or herself?

2 *conceal* Does this mean
   a) to hide or b) to show?

3 *have the gall to* What sort of person is capable of inviting friends to a dinner party at a restaurant and expecting them to pay for themselves?

4 *mixed doubles* What sport does this refer to?

5 *witty line* Is this
   a) an amusing remark or b) a serious remark?

6 *getting round it* Does this mean
   a) to do something willingly or b) to avoid it?

7 *abstention* Do you
   a) accept or b) refuse your ninth glass of wine?

5 How would you describe the overall tone of the passage?

matter-of-fact amusing serious ironic academic   47

There are only two types of dinner party: successes and failures. If you get it right, you will have the satisfaction of being considered a social success by all your acquaintances; if you get it wrong, you will encourage the sort of silences that will explore the full meaning of the word 'awkward'.

The most sensible course of action is never to be a host. But you're a show off and you want the attention, so here goes.

Although it may seem as if it's a contradiction in terms, wherever possible, avoid having dinner parties in your own home. An alternative location that has a number of distinct advantages is a restaurant. Firstly, it enables you to conceal your domestic lifestyle (which, unless you are extremely rich and tasteful, is unlikely to withstand group scrutiny favourably).

Secondly, you don't have to worry about your cooking. Thirdly, and most satisfyingly, you split the cost of the evening with your guests.

If, however, like most people (but, believe me, not all) you don't have the gall to invite your friends to a DP in a restaurant, you should ensure there's an interesting line-up of guests. Therefore your party should comprise three or four couples and a single person.

It is this unfortunate person's role to be patronised and pitied by the couples present. Naturally, you should not be this person. Note: do not entertain if you're partnerless – it makes as much sense as competing in the mixed doubles on your own. Instead, with your arm reassuringly entwined in your partner's, introduce your single friend with a witty line like: 'This is Giles, he can't find a girlfriend.' Everyone will laugh.

Because you're at home, there's no getting round it, you'll have to cook at least some of the food. However, give as much of the responsibility as possible to your guests – starters, puddings, even bits of the main course. Just tell them it's an old Tibetan custom to bring a course, and simply everyone is doing it nowadays. It will be a conversation point.

Talking of talk, there are certain conversational conventions which must be obeyed. Appropriate subject matters are: money, jobs, the relationships of those not present, interior design, and whether you should give money to beggars. It's rude to talk politics, philosophy (unless you're French) or in any informed way about anything.

Still, if after all your efforts, and your conscientious abstention from your ninth glass of wine, it's still a disaster, quietly leave the table and go to bed. Don't worry, your guests will let themselves out. And, anyway, you won't be inviting them again.

WRITING

Write a paragraph describing how you would hold a dinner party. Think about:

food   guests   sitting arrangements   setting
season   clothes   level of formality   conversation
entertainment

_____

_____

_____

_____

_____

_____

_____

_____

_____

LISTENING

1 [cassette] Listen to people talking about four unusual restaurants. Answer the questions by putting the number of the restaurant below in the correct box.
Where would you go if you wanted:

a   to try prehistoric food? ☐

b   to have an exotic meal? ☐

c   to eat as much as you like for a set price? ☐

d   the waiter to choose your menu for you? ☐

1   Rigoletto
2   Snake Bar
3   Big George
4   Jurassic Nosh

2 [cassette] Listen again and write down two dishes or foods you can eat in each restaurant.

_____

_____

_____

_____

Answer Key

Lesson 1
VOCABULARY
2 1 Welsh 2 Russian;
  3 Chinese; 4 Japanese
  5 German 6 French
3 1 Do you speak any of
  these languages?
  2 Would you like to learn
  any of them?
  3 Which do you think are
  particularly difficult to
  learn?
  4 Are any of these
  languages similar to your
  native language?
  5 How long have you been
  learning English?
  6 What languages did you
  study at school?

LISTENING
Language Description
French fast, attractive, serious
Spanish exciting, melodious,
  musical, not difficult
Japanese incredibly hard,
  strange sounds,
  complicated
Arabic difficult, mysterious,
  exotic
German complicated
2 1 aren't they; 2 can't you;
  3 don't you; 4 don't you;
  5 wouldn't you; 6 Let's,
  shall we
3 3 ✓; 5 ✓
4 1 The woman studied
  French at school but she
  can't understand a word
  now.
  2 The man studied Spanish
  at school, but we don't
  know whether he studied
  French.
  4 The woman would like
  to learn Arabic.
  6 Only the man needs
  German for his work.

GRAMMAR
1 1 shall we; 2 could you;
  3 will you; 4 will there;
  5 doesn't she; 6 will you;
  7 are there; 8 can you;
  9 have you; 10 is there
2 1 is it; 2 Have you;
  3 Would you; 4 Are they;
  5 Did they; 6 Haven't you

SOUNDS
1 3, 5 and 6 are real questions.

READING
1 2
2 finish reading the
  newspaper; watch TV;
  phone a friend; have a meal;
  watch TV to digest food
3 1b 2a 3a 4b

Lesson 2
VOCABULARY
1 bow kiss nod kneel
  wave clap cuddle smile
  grin hug shake stretch
  beckon chew laugh
  shrug wink pat spit
  stare blow frown scratch
2 1 laughing; 2 nodded;
  3 shake; 4 staring; 5 chew;
  6 shrugged; 7 blow; 8 bow;
  9 grinned; 10 smiled

SOUNDS
1 /tʃ/: cheek chew
  exchange pinch scratch
  /ʃ/: convention couchette
  friendship shake shrug
  social suspicious
2 Silent r: 1 you<u>r</u> finger;
  2 familiar form, for friends;
  4 far to; 6 taller than, her
  mother; 8 they're very;
  9 near here; 11 stare like
  Used as a link: 1 finge<u>r</u> at
  3 fa<u>r</u> away; 5 fo<u>r</u> ourselves;
  7 quarte<u>r</u> of, hou<u>r</u> ago;
  10 Poo<u>r</u> Anne, a<u>r</u>e unlucky
3 Before a vowel the *r* is
  used as a link.
  Before a consonant it is
  silent.
4 frown – bow; stare – bear;
  born – yawn; though –
  blow; warm – form; put –
  foot; laugh – arm

GRAMMAR
1 1 acg; 2 def; 3 bd
2 1c 2d 3f 4g 5a 6f 7b
3 (1) a; (2) –; (3) –; (4) –;
  (5) The; (6) –; (7) –; (8) –;
  (9) –; (10) –; (11) an;
  (12) a; (13) –; (14) a;
  (15) –; (16) –

READING
2 They bow. Foreigners find
  this difficult because they
  don't know exactly how to
  do it.
3 You can bow: too deeply;

not deeply enough; to the
wrong person; at the wrong
time
4 rank; standing; age; social
  position
5 verbal greetings
6 romantic: France;
  unromantic: Italy; diffident:
  Britain and Italy;
  affectionate: Hungary;
  simple and effective: Spain
  health: parts of Africa,
  Ukraine, Russia, Spain
  Religion: southern
  Germany, Austria
7 1 The first time you meet
  someone. Reply: How do
  you do?
  2 When you already know
  someone
  Reply: Very well, thank you.
8 Because it is a form of
  address in Australia and
  does not require an answer.

LISTENING
3 Speaker 1: d; Speaker 2: a;
  Speaker 3: b; Speaker 4: c
4 Speaker 1: disadvantage:
  felt left out, advantage: had
  more freedom
  Speaker 2: advantage: had
  a wonderful relationship
  with parents, self-sufficient,
  disadvantage: she was a bit
  spoilt, it made her selfish
  Speaker 3: disadvantage:
  you have to establish the
  rules, lots of rows,
  advantage: you get more
  attention until the younger
  children arrive;
  Speaker 4: advantage: older
  children did all the hard
  work and when he was a
  teenager allowed to do
  what he liked,
  disadvantage: spoilt,
  handed-down clothes

Lesson 3
VOCABULARY
1 1 tennis; 2 basketball;
  3 golf; 4 judo; 5 athletics;
  6 figure skating
3 give up; half time; kick off;
  baseball; free kick;
  showjumping

LISTENING
1 a golf; b swimming;
  c motor racing; d cycling;
  e showjumping
2 1d cycling 2a golf 3c motor
  racing 4b swimming
  5e showjumping
3 1 four years; 2 wins;
  3 third; 4 turn; 5 no

GRAMMAR
1 1 are playing; 2 she's
  always asking; 3 arrive;
  4 wins, chooses; 5 are
  leading; 6 watch; 7 are
  walking, is applauding;
  8 spends
2 *Suggested answers*
  2 I wish he wasn't always
  playing computer games.
  3 I wish they didn't sit
  around gossiping about
  people.
  4 I wish he didn't lose so
  much money at the races.
  5 I wish she wouldn't keep
  asking me to take her
  dancing.
  6 I wish I wasn't always
  getting lost.
3 *Suggested answers*
  1 I'm always eating
  chocolate.
  2 The children are always
  fighting.
  3 She only says she enjoys
  going to games.
  4 I wish they didn't have
  such big serves.
  5 All they do is stand in
  queues.

SOUNDS
1 The speaker sounds
  disapproving in sentences
  2, 3 and 4.
2 /ʌ/: current jump club
  under fun
  /ɜː/: turn hurdles fur
  purpose

READING
1 1 rabbit showjumping;
  2 horse showjumping; it's
  cheap and democratic;
  4 Scandinavia; 5 quarantine
  regulations
2 1 jump fences; 2 small;
  3 without training; 4 yes;
  5 other rabbits; 6 no
3 1 true; 2 true; 3 true; 4 no

evidence; 5 no evidence;
6 false

4 1 finding a form of
showjumping that everyone
can afford; 2 they are used
for experiments; 3 rabbit
showjumping; 4 British
rabbits

5 amusing; ironic

Lesson 4

VOCABULARY AND READING

2 1d 2g 3f 4h 5a 6c 7e
8b

3 1 a restaurant in the Barrio
Popular; 2 the main tourist
office; 3 the Prado museum;
4 the Chicote bar; 5 the
Rastro flea market; 6 the
Aqualung or Revolver
clubs; 7 Santiago Bernabéu
stadium; 8 Centro de Arte
Reina Sofia

GRAMMAR AND FUNCTIONS

1 1P 2I 3D 4P 5D 6P 7I
8D

2 1c 2a 3g 4e 5b 6f 7d

4 1 are eating/going to eat;
2 leaves; 3 am catching;
4 'll come; 5 will you
remind; 6 are visiting/ going
to visit; 7 shut; 8 I'm getting;
9 stay; 10 are staying

LISTENING

1 1 ✓; 2 ✓; 3 ✓; 4 ✓; 5 ✓; 6
✓; 7 ✓; 10 ✓

2 *Suggested answers*
1 a stroll; 2 football match;
3 opera; 4 drink cheap
wine; 5 Sunday mornings;
6 souvenirs; 7 local
specialities; 8 well-known
paintings; 9 contemporary
art; 10 sightseeing trip

SOUNDS

1 ✓; 2 ✗; 3 ✗; 4 ✗; 5 ✓;
6 ✓; 7 ✗; 8 ✗

Lesson 5

VOCABULARY

1 first class; long-haul; stand-
by; fast lane; buffet car;
quayside; foothills

2 1 foothills; 2 first class;
3 Long-haul; 4 quayside;
5 buffet car; 6 fast lane;
7 stand-by

3 *Suggested answers*
climate: frost, rainy season,
winter, heat, tropical, sun,
temperature, freezing
geographical features:
foothills, sea, valley, stream

4 *mood*: nostalgic, miserable,
tense, content, romantic,
satisfied, discontented, empty,
optimistic, melancholic
behaviour: cruel, shy, kind,
honest, lazy, vulgar,
reluctant, ruthless

READING

1 3

2 1 true; 2 false; 3 true;
4 false; 5 false

3 2 He hasn't had any major
illnesses.
3 Both his parents are still
alive.
4 He lives somewhere he
likes.
5 He's had a good education.
6 He's got some good
friends.
7 He hasn't suffered too
badly from a broken heart.

4 1 He hasn't travelled very
much.
2 He hasn't got a flashy car.

5 I don't throw things away.
I don't forget things.
I don't make a lot of noise.

GRAMMAR

1 2 I've been bumbling along
for 30 years methodically
collecting minor experience.
5 I've been living with my
adopted dog for five years
now.
6 She has been writing
books all her adult life.
8 They have been living in
South America since 1990.

4 1 a They have finished
travelling.
b The focus is on how long
they've been travelling.
They may or may not have
stopped.
2 a We don't know if he is
still in New York.
b He is no longer in New
York.
3 a We don't know if he is
still training.
b He has finished training.
4 a They're awake now.
b We don't know if they're
still sleeping.
5 a The focus is is on how
many presents she has
bought.
b The focus is on how long
she has spent buying
presents.

SOUNDS

1 first class; long-haul;
stand-by; fast lane; buffet
car; opening hours;

second class; cross channel

2 1 fare; 2 sand; 3 full;
4 prefer; 5 horizon

LISTENING

2 1b 2a 3e 4d 5c

3 Speaker 1 romantic really
contented;
Speaker 2 melancholic,
longing, sadness, romance,
pleasure;
Speaker 3 a good feeling,
satisfied, relaxed, romantic;
Speaker 4 spiritual, very
small and insignificant;
Speaker 5 sad, not happy
thoughts

Lesson 6

VOCABULARY

1 Across: prescription, wound,
blood, heart, cut, chemist,
clinic, consult, sick, injection,
diseases, injury, nurse,
temperature, ambulance
Down: pain, patient, ward,
ointment, ill, tablets, intensive

2 nurse; pain; blood;
temperature; wound;
patient; ambulance;
injury/wound; intensive;
heart; intensive; ward;
consultant; ill; prescriptions

3 Verbs: lie; deceive; report;
humour; consult; appoint;
prescribe; apologise; apply

READING

1 the anniversary of the first
time he and his wife met.

2 h a d g b c e f

3 *Suggested answers*
1 Sandra left a note only
saying she was going away
for a few days.
2 He wasn't worried
because his wife had gone
away like this before.
3 Their relationship had
gone a bit stale since their
daughter had left.
4 He decided to spend the
anniversary on his own in
Paris.
5 He married his wife in
London.

4 A woman's voice behind
me said: 'May I join you?'
Startled, I opened my eyes
and turned around. In a
state of disbelief, I watched
as my wife, holding a bottle
of white wine and a large
bag of fruit, came round
and sat next to me on the
bench. She looked wonderful.

She'd had her hair done
and was wearing a lovely
floral print summer dress.
'Sandra?' I blurted out.
'I was hoping you'd come,'
she smiled.

SOUNDS

2 /k/: psychiatry; crutches;
mechanic; chemist
/tʃ/: wheelchair; crutches;
teacher; bench; watch;
temperature

GRAMMAR

1 *Suggested answers*
1 I took a sip from the
cappuccino …
2 As I was relaxing in the
bath, …
3 I've become boring in my
old age.
4 She'd done this several
times …
5 We had been having a
few problems recently …

2 *Suggested answers*
2 he decided to return to
Paris.
3 a lady asked if she could
join him.
4 he had a bath.
5 he walked to the Tuileries.
6 he remembered that day
25 years ago.
7 she had gone away
several times during their
marriage.
8 he had been working
long hours.
9 he bought a baguette and
salami for lunch.
10 he took the Metro.

LISTENING

1 1B 2A 3F 4E

2 *hair styles*: shortish hair
cropped quite short at the
sides longer on top short
quite thick and springy
thinning a bit slightly
frizzy tied in a bunch at
the back
body size: quite tall very
tall slim a little taller than
average medium build
slender medium height

READING AND WRITING

2 *past perfect simple*: he had
come; he had never gone;
he had done; he had
worked; he had been; he
had had; he had been
past perfect continuous:
had been working; he had
been running

Lesson 7

VOCABULARY

2 breathtaking dramatic
exotic monotonous
perfect picturesque
spectacular stunning
unspoilt

SOUNDS

1 1 rugged; 2 river;
3 courteous; 4 meadow;
5 brow

2 oasis volcano peninsula
earthquake cathedral
fertile waterfall
monotonous geography
scenery dramatic
surrounded paradise

READING

1 1 a region; 2 mountains;
3 a town; 4 a farmhouse

2 1 acd; 2 befgh; 3 bef; 4 bh

3 1 monotonous, spectacular,
unspoilt; 2 spectacular,
lazy, perfect, inexpressibly,
beautiful; 3 beautiful,
attractive, friendly, striking,
elegantly, stunning;
4 irresistible

4 1C 2A 3B 4A

GRAMMAR

1 *Suggested answers*
road bridge town centre
mountain/seaside climate
market garden road/plane
journey pasture land
country market
river mouth mountain
pasture
cliff path mountain peak
garden pond country road
south coast road surface
market/seaside town river
valley
desert/island/mountain
vegetation
cliff/coast/mountain walk

2 1 Passage 1: ... with only a
few centimetres of moisture
falling each year; ... with a
wide variety of marine
wildlife; ... with many
national parks
Passage 2: ... steep green
wooded hills with alpine
meadows
Passage 3: ... with Tudor
timbered houses
Passage 4: ... with the
wooden shutters half-
closed

3 1 beautiful, steep, wooded
hills
2 romantic, ruined, stone
castles

3 spectacular, winding,
single-track roads
4 vast, dry, windswept
plains
5 elegant, two-storey,
marble villa

5 *Suggested answers*
1 It is an exceptionally
beautiful, wild region with
a vast national park.
2 There is a spectacular,
fifty-metre high glacier.
3 The streets are lined with
elegant, six-storey, 19th-
century buildings.
4 The road is steep and
sinuous with shacks along
one side.
5 There are steep, wooded
hills with sheep grazing on
the lower slopes.

6 *Suggested answers*
Passage 1: stretches 1km
across, stands 50m high
Passage 2: high up into, all
around, at the summit, on
the other side, stretched
away, before me, led
steeply down to, spread
out along, along the road
Passage 3: high on,
overlooking, clustered
around, dominating,
beside, looking down
upon, out across
Passage 4: set above, runs
between, at the end of,
rose from, to the top floor,
attached to the back,
beyond that

LISTENING

1 *View 1*: Paddy fields in
China seen from the brow
of a hill.
View 2: The Alps seen from
a plane.
View 3: The south coast of
France seen from a ship on
the sea.

2 Speaker 1: beautiful,
wonderful view,
extraordinary sense of
ordered beauty,
unbelievably beautiful, soft
and gentle
Speaker 2: extraordinary,
breathtaking
Speaker 3: the most
breathtaking view I have
ever seen, magnificent
mountains, magical

3 a2 b1 c3 d1 e3 f2

4 a Although it was summer,
some of the higher peaks
were covered in snow.
b There was an

extraordinary sense of
ordered beauty as if the
whole scene was an
imitation of nature.
c Then rising out of the
clouds were the
magnificent mountains.
d ... when we reached the
brow of the hill there was a
wonderful view of the
paddy fields.
e Above the sea was a
narrow strip of land but we
were too far out to sea to
make out any details.
f ... and I could see rivers
gently winding their way
through the valleys.

Lesson 8

VOCABULARY

1 1 watching, hear/notice;
2 see, hear; 3 felt, saw;
4 listening to, heard/saw/
noticed; 5 listening to; 6 hear;
7 saw/noticed; 8 hear

2 1 groan: the only sound;
2 sour: the only taste;
3 creak: the only sound;
4 bark: a sound made by a
dog; 5 scented: the only
smell

READING

1 1 an elderly man, his son
and daughter-in-law
2 a dog
3 hearing, touch

2 1c 2e 3a 4d 5b

3 1 false; 2 true; 3 true; 4 false;
5 true; 6 false; 7 true

4 1 whining; barked; howled;
growled
2 the dog was alert – tense;
warning bark of alarm;
trembling with fear; made
him shiver; infected now
by her own panic .
3 a grabbed; b stroked;
c shove
4 e scratch
5 b leap; c bound

5 The son and daughter-in-
law were amused when the
father told them the story.
The elderly man was
uncomfortable when he
was lying on the bed with
Granta next to him because
it was very hot.
The man was impatient to
be left on his own.
The man was frightened by
the dog's behaviour.
The man was ashamed to
tell his son and daughter-
in-law that he had hit out

at something that wasn't
there.
The man was relieved
when he was finally on his
own in the house.

GRAMMAR

1 2 Smiling at each other,
they walked away.
3 Getting out of bed, he
grabbed his stick.
4 Growling at the thing in
the corner, she prepared to
attack.
5 Finding the door open,
he went in.
6 Coming downstairs, she
saw the car drive off.
7 Crossing the road, I
noticed him walk into a
shop.
8 Seeing it was raining, she
took an umbrella.

2 2 Tourists going to Italy in
the spring are very sensible.
3 Foreigners visiting the city
usually stay in the centre.
4 The man walking towards
us comes from the university.
5 People living in that part
of town are very lucky.
6 The family living next
door have just moved in.

3 *Suggested answers*
1 scratching; 2 hit/hitting;
3 whispering;
4 grab/grabbing;
5 groan/groaning;
6 sigh/sighing

LISTENING

1 A snake, perhaps a cobra

2 1 leaving her father-in-law
alone; 2 because he always
made fun of people who
believed in ghosts; 3 train
and taxi; 4 looks like a
battleground; 5 she sees a
snake; 6 the snake must
have got in; 7 she made
fun of her father-in-law;
8 it might upset him more

SOUNDS

2 *silent*: sighed frightened
though thought taught
eighty
/f/: roughly laugh tough
cough enough

Lesson 9

LISTENING

1 Speaker 1: first and last day
at kindergarten, unhappy
Speaker 2: first riding
lesson, happy
Speaker 3: the day she was

accused of stealing,
unhappy

2 *Suggested answers*
Speaker 1: screaming at the
top of the stairs, outdoor
staircase with a concrete
balcony, glass door, bare
room with toys
Speaker 2: the journey to
the riding stables, mini bus,
trying on riding hats, the
elastic under his chin, smell
of saddles, covered in mud
Speaker 3: smell of new
blouse, doing up her tie,
the headmistress holding
out the empty bag of sweets,
being accused of stealing

READING
1 very little
2 I cannot even remember;
nor can I picture; I do
vaguely remember; I have
a blurred memory of; that's
all that comes back to me
3 1 He can't remember what
his classroom looked like.
He can't remember the
faces of the two women
who ran the kindergarten.
2 He vaguely remembers
trying to tie his shoelaces.
He vaguely remembers
being made to eat soggy
cabbage and greasy
sausages at lunchtime.
3 He remembers the
journey to and from school.
He remembers racing at
great tricycle speeds down
the middle of the road and
taking the corner on two
wheels.

GRAMMAR
1 1 I remember going up an
outdoor staircase with a
concrete balcony.
2 I remember seeing a bare
room with toys.
3 I remember seeing a
glass door
2 1 I remember the journey
to the riding stables.
2 I remember the feel of
the elastic under my chin.
3 I remember the
marvellous smell of the
saddles.
3 1 I remember the
headmistress calling us into
assembly.
2 I remember her holding
up an empty bag of sweets.
3 I remember her grabbing
me by the arm.

READING
1 1 a master at Repton
school; 2 mathematics;
3 yes; 4 no; 5 no
2 *appearance*: vast ungainly;
drooping bloodhound
cheeks; filthy clothes;
creaseless flannel trousers;
a brown tweed jacket with
patches; bits of dried food
on the lapels
personality: eccentric old
bachelor; neither dull nor
colourless; charmer
3 1b 2b 3a 4b 5a
4 amusing

GRAMMAR
1 There used to be about
thirty masters …
He used to wear creaseless
trousers …
He would wear …
His lessons used to consist
of an endless series …
His lessons would consist
of …
2 … so that the subject of
mathematics would never
have to be discussed
… never used to have …
He would come lumbering
into the room … He used
to come … We would wait
expectantly … We used to
wait … … he would say …
… he used to say …
Corker would proceed to
draw … Corker used to
proceed to …
3 1 I'm not used to; 2 is not
used to; 3 get used to;
4 am not used to, got used
to; 5 is not used to; 6 get
used to; 7 to get used to;
8 am not used to, get used to

Lesson 10
VOCABULARY
1 1 judge; 2 prosecution;
3 defence lawyer;
4 defendant; 5 jury; 6 court;
7 magistrate
2 e d b h g a c f
3 1 sentenced, prison,
suspended, prosecution,
appeal
2 guilty, court, extradited,
sentence, fined
3 judge, forged, extradited,
convicted
4 guilty, jury, charged,
case, court, lawyer

Lesson 11
VOCABULARY
1 1 scissors; 2 tin opener;
3 saucepan; 4 spade;
5 corkscrew; 6 drill;
7 broom; 8 spanner

LISTENING
1 1 corruption and
conspiracy; 2 libel and
harassment; 3 grievous
bodily harm
2 1 suspended jail sentence;
2 fine and court order to
keep the peace; 3 jail
sentence
3 1 The men fixed football
matches; 2 The man
verbally abused and
harassed a neighbour;
3 The driver head-butted
another driver.

GRAMMAR
1 1 ✓ 4 ✓ 5 ✓ 6 ✓
2 1 must/should; 2 have to;
3 must/have to; 4 must;
5 mustn't; 6 should;
7 must/have to; 8 mustn't
3 *Suggested answers*
2 They should have
checked the shoes before
stealing them.
They shouldn't have taken
the shoes without checking
them first.
3 He should have checked
there was a golf course.
He shouldn't have said he
had been playing golf.
4 He should have chosen
something else to steal.
He shouldn't have sniffed
the glue.

READING
3 1 false; 2 no evidence;
3 false; 4 no evidence;
5 false, 6 no evidence;
7 true
4 The moon belongs to all of
mankind.
There is no answer to the
question about the
nationality of a baby born
in space.
The countries which launch
satellites and rockets are
responsible for the debris
and the pollution.
There is no specific answer
to the question about
whether anyone can send
anything into space, but we
learn that everything being
sent into space must be
registered.

2 1 relieve; 2 spill; 3 stings,
smear; 4 swallowing;
5 soften; 6 tickle; 7 creep;
8 shelter

READING
1 feeling tired or unwell
dehydration oxygen
deficiency dizziness
fainting stiffness cramps
2 1b 2c 3d 4a 5e 6f
3 1 dizziness; 2 stiffness;
3 limber up; 4 enhance;
5 offset; 6 restrict; 7 shape;
8 exacerbate

GRAMMAR
1 *Suggested answers*
2 Eat foods containing
vitamins A and E in order
to build up your immune
system.
3 Take exercise in order to
offset the effects of
reduced air pressure.
Take exercise in order not
to feel stiff.
4 Drink a lot of water in
order to avoid dehydration.
5 Drink carrot juice before
flying to help avoid oxygen
deficiency.
6 Have light, frequent
meals in order not to suffer
from dizziness and fainting.
Have light, frequent meals
in order to avoid problems
of blood circulation.
2 *Suggested answers*
2 You should wear eye
pads and earplugs so that
you sleep better.
3 You should avoid
drinking alcohol so that
you don't restrict the
brain's oxygen intake.
4 You should wear loose
clothes so that you don't
feel stiff and get cramp.
5 You should get some
exercise before the flight so
that you offset the effects
on the body of reduced air
pressure.
6 You should consult your
doctor before flying if you
are on medication so that
you don't suffer from
unpleasant side-effects.
3 *Suggested answers*
1 Avoid drinking coffee so
that you don't increase
body dehydration.
2 Avoid smoking so that
you don't decrease your
blood oxygen level.
3 When you arrive stay in

bright light so that your body stays alert.
4 Try aromatherapy oils so that you stay calm.

LISTENING
1 a ✓ b ✓ c ✓ f ✓ g ✓
2 a solves crosswords; b no point in it, just looks attractive; c for mixing and serving drinks; f you can see them in the dark; g gives you all the possible word combinations for Scrabble
3 1 mad; 2 easy, fun; 3 ridiculous; 4 useful

GRAMMAR
1 *People*: careless clever generous (un)kind stupid thoughtful
Situations: easy essential important (un)necessary rare useful useless
2 1 for; 2 for; 3 of; 4 for; 5 of; 6 for; 7 of; 8 of

SOUNDS
1 1 useful; 2 easy; 3 kind, weekend; 4 essential, good grade, exams; 5 thoughtless, birthday; 6 important, grandchildren; 7 generous, presents; 8 careless, lose, book

Lesson 12

VOCABULARY
1 and 2 *Suggested answers*
fry: eggs, onions, potatoes
grill: steak, sausages
roast: chicken, pork
stew: apples, meat
boil: milk, rice, vegetables
poach: fish, eggs
steam: vegetables, puddings
2 Across: 1 pepper; 3 chop; 6 dice; 8 bread; 9 foil; 10 fry; 11 carrots; 13 egg; 14 raw; 15 yogurt; 19 boil; 20 cheese; 22 snack; 23 cakes; 24 toast; 25 steam; 26 wrap
Down: 2 peel; 3 calorie; 4 oil; 5 poach; 7 chips; 8 banana; 12 nuts; 16 onion; 17 greasy; 18 chicken; 19 butter; 21 fat; 22 stew

GRAMMAR
1 1 will cook; 2 go, have; 3 wins, will become; 4 was, would work; 5 had, would cook; 6 is, will have

READING
1 3
2 1f 2e 3b 4c 5a 6d
3 *Suggested answers*
1 You should avoid holding dinner parties in your own home.
2 You should make sure there is a decent line-up of guests.
3 You should get your guests to bring some of the food.
4 You shouldn't discuss politics.
5 If it is a disaster, you should go to bed discreetly.
4 1a; 2a; 3 someone who is shameless and has a lot of self-assurance; 4 tennis; 5a; 6b; 7b
5 *Suggested answer*
amusing, ironic

LISTENING
1 a4 b2 c3 d1
2 Jurassic Nosh: deer's tail served with nettles and dandelions, grilled radishes, funny soups, spelt soup made with a neolithic-type wheat, berries, honey
Snake Bar: marinaded sea bear with fresh ginger, alligator, snake sandwiches, ostrich salad
Rigoletto: artichokes, aubergines, cauliflower, courgettes, tuna, creamy sauces
Big George: salads, salami, pâté, garlic bread, chilli beans
3 *Suggested answers*
1 I'd go to Rigoletto
chats with them for a few minutes
you are adventurous
2 we go to the Snake Bar
you can eat a snake sandwich or an ostrich salad
you may be disappointed
3 you will be served strange food
you may be shocked by the way the food looks
you don't like strange food
4 I'd go to Big George.
are hungry
it is very late at night

Lesson 13

VOCABULARY
1 1 hacker; 2 laptop; 3 database; 4 modem;

5 virus; 6 download
2 1 hackers, database; 2 viruses, hard disk; 3 laptop; 4 silicon chip; 5 Internet; 6 online

GRAMMAR
1 1 have not been evaluated; 2 is currently being prepared; 3 were not prosecuted; 4 be disconnected; 5 will be improved; 6 be stored, be seriously damaged
2 1 The hard disk was destroyed by a virus.
2 A flaw was discovered in the bank's computer system by the hacker group.
3 The whole car was covered with snow.
4 The fields all around the farm have been flooded with canal water.
5 New ways of forecasting the weather are being developed by researchers.
6 Reliable 36-hour forecasting will be made possible by new mathematical techniques.
7 Extensive damage to the police computer system may have been caused by a power cut.
8 More sophisticated security measures should be introduced by software producers.

READING
1 1C 2A 3B
2 A: has been transformed, is given, are tapped, are also hooked up
B: it is feared, was blamed, is steadily spreading/has been steadily spreading, is spent, is wasted/is being wasted
3 2
4 1d 2c 3e 4a 5b
5 2 ✓; 3 ✓; 5 ✓; 6 ✓

GRAMMAR
1 2 Someone is needed to take the decision for them.
3 The report still has to be faxed.
4 I still have to be introduced to his boss.
5 The system needs to be checked.
6 The document will have to be printed.
2 2 He doesn't like being beaten at chess by computers.

3 They're worried about the system being damaged by lightning.
4 I'd like to be shown how this word processor works.
5 He wants to be advised about suitable software.
6 Steps to control electronic espionage should be taken.
7 New ways of increasing computer powers must be found.

SOUNDS
1 Being connected to an e-mail system is useful.
2 She's nervous about being charged too much.
3 She's looking forward to being invited over.
4 They are being contacted directly.

LISTENING
1 1 ✓; 2 ✗; 3 ✓; 4 ✗; 5 ✓; 6 ✗
2 W: 1 3 5
   M: 2 4 6
3 1 It has destroyed the ability of a whole generation to do simple maths.
2 That's ridiculous! It's just a time-saver.
3 Just imagine a teacher who can't spell or write properly.
4 We won't be judging people on the way they write but on their ideas.
5 Already children spend more time in front of the screen and less time in books.
6 Computers will never replace the human brain.

Lesson 14

VOCABULARY
1 *Suggested answers*
religion: baptism hymn beliefs faith worship services ritual prayers ceremonies spiritual church
cultural identity: custom ancestor discrimination ethnic minority dialect stereotype traditions ceremonies folklore community heritage prejudice costume
2 ancestors, customs/beliefs/traditions, prayers, worship, faith/community
4 *Suggested answers*
people: laid-back anti-conformist racist popular

materialistic cosmopolitan *places*: popular peaceful isolated cosmopolitan

SOUNDS
Protestant <u>ancestors</u>, fro<u>m</u> Europe, manage<u>d</u> <u>to</u>, an<u>d</u> uniqu<u>e</u>, wa<u>y of</u>, Religion <u>is</u> all <u>important in</u>, prayer<u>s</u> are, no<u>t expected to</u>

READING
1 3

3 1f 2c 3e 4b 5a 6g 7d

GRAMMAR
1 1 ✓; 2 ✗; 3 ✓; 4 ✓; 5 ✓; 6 ✗; 7 ✗

2 1 animals; 2 farmers; 3 They live in very isolated places, the children; 4 The community is very close-knit; 5 region; 6 people; 7 The children get little experience of life outside the community

3 1 that; 3 who

4 1 The household we visited consisted of eight people.
2 The people we met on the trip are coming to stay next weekend.
3 The motel we stayed at was on the freeway out of town.
4 The restaurant we ate at in the evening is downtown.

5 1 A region which is devoted mainly to stock-breeding, …
2 … the practice of hospitality which was introduced by the Spanish …
3 … for travellers who wish to cross it …
4 … and the hospitality which is offered there is special, if not unique.
5 Travellers who are accustomed to short distances are sure to have forgotten something …
6 Vehicles which have been abandoned by the roadside are a common sight.
7 … there will be a room which is reserved for the guest …

6 1 There is a youth club for local children interested in sport.
2 The man working in the museum comes from California.
3 Cattle grazing on the plains are a common sight.
4 The food served there is very special.

5 People wanting to have a good time are advised to go downtown.
6 The country accepting the most immigrants is the USA.

LISTENING
1 1 Cedar Rapids Iowa State, USA
2 The Czech Republic (Moravia)
3 Her grandparents came in the 1840s.
4 Because of drought and crop failure and advertisements and rumours promising gold

2 Thirty per cent, Czech; 2 the Czech Museum and Library; 3 advertisements and rumours of gold; 4 a strong sense of their Czech identity; 5 Czech festivals

3 It is managing to retain it.

Lesson 15

READING
1 3

2 1 nostagic and melancholic; 2 envious; 3 unwilling to continue the conversation; 4 hesitant

3 kind, concerned, cheerful, confident, relaxed, polite

4 2 I wish I was at home with my family. 3 I wish the man hadn't started a conversation. 4 I wish the lift had arrived more quickly. 5 I wish I hadn't taken the lift and had walked down the stairs.

GRAMMAR
2 *Suggested answers*
1 …the lift goes down.
2 … the numbers of the floors ticking away.
3 … started to think about his life. 4 … to spend so much time travelling.
5 … to enjoy it. 6 … at home with his family.
7 … a woman standing there. 8 …if the lift was going up. 9 … that it was going down. 10 … the lift continued its descent.

3 *Suggested answers*
1 wouldn't have met the man. 2 the man wouldn't have started talking about the Bill Bryson story
3 the writer wouldn't have thought about his life.
4 he would have ben much happier. 5 the woman

would have got in. 6 the writer would probably have panicked.

5 1 ✗; 2 ✓; 3 ✗; 4 ✓; 5 ✓; 6 ✗

SOUNDS
2 They are all compound words. windscreen clipboard handbag seatbelt countdown football postcard setback
3 All the underlined /r/ sounds are silent.

READING
1 1 ✗ 2 ✓ 3 ✓ 4 ✗ 5 ✓

2 1 the end of the story; 2 to the explosion; 3 Because the lift is going down; 4 the business card; 5 A life assurance policy

WRITING
1 I opened my eyes. I don't know how much time passed, but it was at least a minute, perhaps a good deal more. My companion was staring at his attaché case. He held it to his ear, shook it once and pushed it away in disgust.
'You see?' he said to me.
'You see? Nothing goes right any more.'

Lesson 16

VOCABULARY
1 1 up, in; 2 for, across; 3 up; 4 down; 5 up, away; 6 on ;7 on; 8 up with

2 2 caught on; 3 turned down; 4 wrote down; 5 brought up, talk it over; 6 took up; 7 took off; 8 turned off *or* put out; 9 sit down; 10 came out

GRAMMAR
1 1 Type 3; 2 Type 4; 3 Type 3; 4 Type 1; 5 Type 2; 6 Type 1; 7 Type 4; 8 Type 2

2 look at: Type 1; take over: Type 2; carry on: Type 3; hand over: Type 2; pay back: Type 2; get on with: Type 4; put away: Type 2; get over: Type 3

3 2 He handed it over.
3 He did away with them on the disk.
4 He gave it up.
5 She asked for it/one.
6 He put them away.
7 The recording company turned it down.

8 I've been thinking carefully about it

READING
2 1A 2B 3A 4B 5B 6A

4 1 the street musician; 2 the part of a song that is repeated several times; 3 the barrel-organ; 4 the traditions of the past

5 1 false; 2 true; 3 true; 4 true

6 *Passage A*: takes up, singing along with, wrapped up in, pass by, walk on, go on, head for, pull down over
Passage B: put on, set up, shut up in, pass through

7 be wrapped up in; walk on; set up
put on; head for; shut up in; go on

LISTENING
1 *Suggested answers*
How/Why did you choose the violin? Where/Why When did you first study music? How long have you been in the orchestra? How often/When/Where do you rehearse? How old were you when you started to play? How many musicians are there? What/How many other instruments do you play?

2 1 How long have you been in the orchestra?
2 Where did you first study music?
3 How old were you when you started to play?
4 How often do you rehearse?
5 How many musicians are there?
6 What other instruments do you play?
7 How did you choose the violin?

3 1 She has been in the orchestra for twelve years. 2 She studied at York University and the Royal Academy, London. 3 She was five. 4 She practises every day, but orchestra rehearsals vary. 5 There are about 89. 6 She can play the piano and flute. 7 She is attracted to instruments that reflect her voice.

SOUNDS

1 1 He wrote it down.
   2 She looked at him.
   3 They came up with it.
   4 He turned them down.
   5 We will have to put up
     with it.
   6 I threw it away.
2 /k/: choir orchestra chord
     anachronistic chorus
   /tʃ/: charts beach scratch
     pitch lunch

Lesson 17

VOCABULARY

1 a can of soup, a carton of
   cream, a sack of potatoes, a
   bottle of wine, a jar of jam,
   a packet of crisps, a box of
   matches, a tube of
   toothpaste
2 2 furniture because it is the
   only manufactured product
   3 beer because it isn't a
   dairy product
   4 newspaper because it
   isn't a container
   5 sack because it doesn't
   hold liquid
   6 drop because it refers to
   liquid
3 a slice of bread, a piece of
   cake, a pinch of salt, a litre
   of milk, a rasher of bacon
4 furniture, toothpaste,
   rubbish, trousers, fun,
   money, weather, music,
   research, news, advice,
   accommodation, information
5 1 furniture; 2
   accommodation; 3 news;
   4 advice; 5 fun;
   6 information; weather

READING

1 1
2 thrift electricity milk
   frugality research
   alcohol clothes petrol
   make-up jeans money
3 1 She buys second-hand
   clothes.
   2 She only buys in
   ordinary shops if there is a
   special offer.
   3 She spends very little on
   food and clothes
   4 She uses cheap, bulk-
   bought shampoo.
4 restaurants, alcohol,
   cigarettes, junk-food,
   magazines, new clothes
5 1 weary; 2 surplus; 3 pare
   down; 4 thrifty; 5 leftovers;
   6 core; 7 ruthless; 8 scrimp;
   9 viable; 10 prior

LISTENING AND VOCABULARY

1 1 borrowing cash; 2 bank
   loans; 3 cash cards;
   4 exchanging foreign
   currency
2 1 account, overdrawn,
   mortgage; 2 branch,
   interest, loans; 3 building
   society, withdrawals;
   4 exchange rate, traveller's
   cheques

SOUNDS

1 We've had a great deal
   of trouble lately.
2 Can you lend me some
   cash, please?
3 It's made of glass.
4 I'll draw some money
   out tonight.

GRAMMAR

1 1 few; 2 little; 3 a little;
   4 few; 5 a little; 6 a few
2 1 hardly any; 2 a great deal
   of; 3 several; 4 enough;
   5 much; 6 some;
   7 much/any

Lesson 18

READING

1 2
2 1 smart money;
   2 intelligent clothes;
   3 interactive TV; 4 animal
   spare parts
3 successful: personal
   computer, CD player,
   satellite dish, microwave,
   pocket calculator, home
   food freezer, credit cards
   unsuccessful: quadrophonic
   discs, Wankel rotary
   engine, soya bean diet
4 1 The examples of things
   that were expected to
   become successful but didn't.
   2 There will be no need to
   go through a central
   processing agency.
   3 Because they regulate
   body temperature.
   4 dieters, sports players
   5 TV
   6 We will be able to
   participate by choosing
   how we want to view
   something, buy things, etc.
   7 medicine

GRAMMAR

1 1 will be using; 2 will have
   replaced; 3 will be wearing;
   4 will have replaced; 5 will
   be participating; 6 will be
   performing

SOUNDS

The underlined letters are
pronounced.
1 You won't just lose
   weight.
2 Old-fashioned notes.
3 credit card
4 cashpoint machine
5 the best part of 25 years

LISTENING

1 1 population 2 famine
   3 war 4 environment
   5 energy resources
   The speaker is generally
   pessimistic.
2 1 false 2 false 3 true
   4 true 5 true 6 false 7 false
3 1 Family planning schemes
   have failed to slow down
   the population explosion.
   2 By the year 2025, the
   world population will have
   increased to 8.5 billion.
   6 We are still dependent on
   oil and nuclear power.
   7 They do not finance them
   because they do not want
   to lose political control.

Lesson 19

VOCABULARY

1 verbs: believe consider
   expect know remain
   think understand
   nouns: belief consideration
   expectation fact
   knowledge myth remains
   remainder thought
   understanding
   adjectives: considerable
   expectant factual
   knowledgeable knowing
   mythical remaining
   thoughtful understanding
   understandable
   adverbs: considerably
   expectantly factually
   knowledgeably knowingly
   thoughtfully
   understandably
2 1 fiction; 2 omen;
   3 mystery; 4 curse; 5 legend;
   6 superstition; 7 soul;
   8 spell; 9 hoax; 10 fact

READING AND GRAMMAR

1 human souls, witches
2 unlucky: if first seen in
   the year was brown, it
   meant you would eat
   humble food – not be
   prosperous; three together;
   one flying at night; red
   butterflies were witches
   lucky: if first seen in the
   year was white, it meant

prosperity; a butterfly
hovering over a corpse
meant everlasting
happiness; a golden
butterfly hovering over a
dying person was a good
omen
3 the soul at death was
thought to leave the body
the soul-butterfly is thought
to fly abroad ...
Burmese children are
taught never to awaken
the newly dead were
thought to be sometimes
visible in the form of a
butterfly
a golden butterfly was
considered to be a very
good omen
to see three together is
considered unlucky
to see one flying at night is
believed to be a death omen
red butterflies were thought
to be witches
4 It was thought that the
soul at death left the
body...
It is thought that the soul-
butterfly flies abroad when
its owner sleeps.
It was thought that the
newly dead were
sometimes visible in the
form of a butterfly.
It was considered that a
golden butterfly was a very
good omen.
It is believed that to see
one flying at night is a
death omen.
It is considered that to see
three together is unlucky.
It was thought that they
were witches.

LISTENING

1 1 bat; 2 black cat;
   3 horseshoe; 4 ladder;
   5 mirror; 6 umbrella
2 1 three times round a
   house; fine weather to
   come
   2 into a house or on board
   a ship; runs across the path
   in front of you
   3 good luck; hang it up
   4 walking under a ladder;
   you see a dog
   5 seven years' bad luck;
   her future husband
   6 open an umbrella in a
   house; bring rain
3 1 Witches were said to
   turn themselves into bats.
   It is thought to be lucky if a

bat falls on someone.

2 In Britain the black cat is considered lucky.

It has been regarded as a holy and a diabolical beast.

3 A horseshoe lying in the road should not be passed by. It should be nailed over the house door.

4 It is considered unlucky to walk under a ladder.

It was believed that to reach through the rungs for anything was unlucky.

5 It is commonly thought that to break a mirror will bring seven years' bad luck.

The face of her future husband would be seen looking over the woman's shoulder.

6 To open an umbrella in the house is said to be unlucky.

If an umbrella is opened during fine weather it will bring rain.

SOUNDS

1 w h w p g b
2 1 wounded; 2 burial;
3 mouth; 4 move

READING

1 1 It was destroyed by an earthquake.

2 A tidal wave might have washed over it.

3 A volcano could have blown part of it into the ocean.

4 The continent was thought to have been submerged in the Atlantic Ocean.

5 It may have been the mythical name for North America.

2 1 false; 2 true; 3 false; 4 true; 5 false; 6 true

3 1 an earthquake couldn't destroy a continent.

2 it is described as a mountainous country.

3 because the description suggests that it was too big to be destroyed by a volcano.

4 because continental drift is too slow to explain its disappearance.

GRAMMAR

1 ..could an earthquake account for the sinking...

An earthquake might have destroyed part...

...it might have been at least partly submerged...

A tidal wave might have washed over Atlantis...

And a volcanic eruption could have blown part of...

...could there be a geological explanation...

Atlantis must have occupied the present position...

So could Atlantis have been North America...

2 1a: certainly didn't happen like that; b: possibly didn't happen like that; 2a: certainly did; b: possibly did; 3a: certainly didn't; b: possibly didn't

3 1 Human beings may/might have existed long before the scientists' estimates.

2 There may/might have been some extraordinary global catastrophe.

3 Atlantis may/might have existed after all.

4 The Greek gods could have been people who …

5 The dinosaurs can't have been destroyed by a comet …

6 Extra-terrestrial beings can't/couldn't have visited Earth.

7 The Vikings must have reached North America.

8 Atlantis may/might have been a small island in the Aegean.

Lesson 20

GRAMMAR

1 1 coffee; 2 car; 3 camcorder; 4 watch; 5 exercise machine; 6 face cream; 7 underwear; 8 air conditioning; 9 emergency medical alarm; 10 colour film

2 *Suggested answers*

1 The slogan claims that the aroma of the coffee gives you an idea of its rich taste.

2 The slogan suggests that although the car has a good engine, that isn't its only interesting feature.

3 This ad claims that the camcorder is small and easy to carry with you when you travel.

4 This slogan doesn't claim any particular qualities but describes its general function of time-keeping in a witty manner.

5 The slogan suggests that you can get rid of your excess kilos around your waist by using the exercise machine.

6 The slogan claims that the face cream is not greasy on your skin and continues to protect you all day.

7 The ad boasts that this underwear is almost as comfortable as wearing nothing at all.

8 The slogan warns that being cold is not good for you and therefore air conditioning is the answer.

9 This slogan promises that you only have to press a button and someone will come to help you.

10 The ad promises that this brand of film produces better colour photos.

3 1 He claimed that its petrol consumption was very reasonable even at high speeds.

2 She ordered Jim to come up with a new advertising campaign for the autumn.

3 She complained that she had bought an unknown brand of ketchup and the kids wouldn't touch it.

4 She claimed she had tried it out on the children's clothes and it had really worked.

5 He asked her what brand of washing powder she used.

6 He promised he would stop smoking if cigarettes went up in price.

7 He said that they might go to Madeira for the winter.

8 He boasted that it tasted better than any other brand on the market.

4 *Suggested answers*

1 'They want to stay an extra night.'

2 'I'll be very quiet when I come in.'

3 'There'll be a speed trap on the motorway.'

4 'I know the area very well.'

5 'I shouldn't stay out too late.'

6 'If it happens again, I'll go to the police.'

7 'Why don't we go out for a meal?'

8 'I'm afraid, I behaved very badly at the party.'

READING AND VOCABULARY

3 3

4 1 There are advertisements on the lavatory door.

2 You are not distracted by anything else.

3 Because they target the audiences likely to use the toilets.

4 They didn't like the idea of their business being associated with toilet smells.

5 Because people who go to classy restaurants are not considered likely to wear sneakers.

6 in discos

SOUNDS

1 /ɒ/: promise, product, cosmetics, sponsor, controversial

/əʊ/: promote, slogan, photo, global, bonus

/ə/: promote, commercial, complain, confess

/ʌ/: wonder, money, company, come, colour

2 promise, product, cosmetics, sponsor, controversial, promote, slogan, photo, global, bonus, promote, commercial, complain, confess, wonder, money, company, come, colour

VOCABULARY

1 1 promoting; 2 global; 3 product; 4 controversial; 5 commercial; 6 sponsored; 7 bonus; 8 money

2 advertisement admission analysis appeal complaint promise promotion suggestion threat warning

LISTENING

2 1 3 4 6 7 9 10

3 1 The ad promised they would fly with a well-known airline.

2 It promised that the flight would be direct from London to Paris.

3 It said that they would be taken by taxi from the airport to the hotel.

4 It said the hotel was in a unique historic area of Paris.

5 The ad promised a luxury double-bedroom with adjoining bath and toilet.

6 The ad promised a view of Montmartre.

7 The ad said it would be a cheap trip.

3 Complete these sentences.

1 If I wanted to take friends for a surprise meal in Brussels,_____
_____.

When customers come into Rigoletto, the owner _____
_____.

You will enjoy Rigoletto provided
_____
_____.

2 When we want an unusual evening out with friends in Rotterdam, _____
_____.

If you go to Snake Bar at lunchtime,
_____
_____.

Always phone beforehand if you want a rare delicacy, otherwise _____
_____.

3 If you go to Jurassic Nosh, _____
_____.

When you are served at Jurassic Nosh,
_____
_____.

You will enjoy Jurassic Nosh unless
_____
_____.

4 If I was very hungry _____
_____.

You will appreciate Big George as long as you
_____
_____.

You will get a meal at Big George, even if
_____
_____.

WRITING

1 What is the most unusual restaurant you have been to? Write a few lines describing it.
_____
_____
_____

2 Which of the restaurants in *Listening* activity 1 would you like to eat at? Is there one which you would not go to? Write a paragraph explaining your reasons.
_____
_____
_____
_____
_____
_____
_____

13 | *Hi-tech dreams or nightmares?*

VOCABULARY

1 Match the definitions below with words or expressions in this list.

hacker   virus   database   online   hard disk
download   laptop   software   modem   keyboard
interface   hardware   Internet   silicon chip

1   an amateur computer enthusiast who keys into computer systems for fun
2   a portable computer
3   a collection of information accessible by computer
4   a device which connects computers to the telephone line
5   an undesirable computer program
6   send information via a computer modem system

2 Complete these sentences with words from the list above.

1   A small group of _____ keyed into the _____ of a German bank in order to expose security risks.
2   Some _____ are harmless and amusing, but others can destroy the _____ of a computer.
3   Thieves inadvertently stole top secret Foreign Office plans when they took a _____ computer from an official's unattended car.
4   A lightning strike can destroy the _____ at the heart of a computer.
5   Freedom of information exchange was one of the founding premises of the _____.
6   Japanese marriage specialists are offering the first _____ Internet wedding service.

GRAMMAR

1 Complete these sentences using a suitable passive form of the verb in brackets.

1   The effects of the project on the participating businesses _____ (not/evaluate) by researchers.
2   A final report _____ (currently/prepare) and will soon be available.
3   The hackers _____ (not/prosecute) because the laws at the time made no provision for electronic crime.
4   Computers should _____ (disconnect) while a storm rages.
5   They expose flaws in computer systems in the hope that security measures _____ (improve).
6   Copies of important information should always _____ (store) in a different location because in the event of a fire or flooding computers could _____ (seriously/damage).

2 Rewrite the sentences in the passive. Use *by* or *with*.

1   A virus destroyed the hard disk.

   _____

   _____.

2   The hacker group discovered a flaw in the bank's computer system.

   _____

   _____.

3   Snow covered the whole car.

   _____

   _____.

4   Canal water has flooded the fields all around the farm.

   _____

   _____.

5 Researchers are developing new ways of forecasting the weather.

_____
_____.

6 New mathematical techniques will make reliable 36-hour forecasting possible.

_____
_____.

7 A power cut may have caused extensive damage to the police computer system.

_____
_____.

8 Software producers should introduce more sophisticated security measures.

_____
_____.

READING

1 Look quickly at articles A, B and C on this page and on page 52 and match the headings with the articles.

1 **Can humans compete with silicon superbrains?**

2 **Villagers adapt to laboratory life**

3 **HI-TECH DISASTER THREATENS POLICE COMPUTER SYSTEMS**

2 Read articles A and B. Complete the articles by putting the verbs in brackets in the passive. Make sure you choose the correct tense.

3 Read article C and tick (✓) the statement which best summarises what the article is about.

1 The dangers of computers taking over humans.

2 The evolution of artificial intelligence and computer technology.

3 The superiority of computer chess programs over human players.

4 The limits of the computer's brain.

4 Five sentences have been removed from article C. Choose from the sentences (a to e) the one which fits each gap (1 to 5).

a If computers are to think and learn, an alternative technology must be found.

b This has led to speculation about the danger of humans ultimately being controlled by a breed of super-computer that evolves of its own will.

c I was greatly consoled to learn that I am not alone in my shame.

d So it is particularly galling to be systematically beaten by the chess program on my laptop.

e World champion Garry Kasparov, who said he would never be beaten by a computer, lies vanquished.

5 Tick (✓) the statements which express the writer's views.

1 The writer is worried about the future because he thinks that one day humans will be controlled by computers.

2 Silicon technology will have to be replaced if computers are to become more sophisticated.

3 Computers can never have a will of their own.

4 Computers already have emotions.

5 Chess programs play better than even the great chess masters.

6 There are two major areas of research being investigated which hopefully will enable computers to become more powerful.

A

A remote village in the centre of Sweden _____ (transform) into the world's most computerised community. The village of Are – population of 800 – has for the past year been acting as a living laboratory for information technology as researchers are examining what happens when an entire community _____ (give) computers, software and training.

Computer keyboards _____ (tap) in the back rooms of the village bakery, T-shirt manufacturer, taxi firm, clothes shops, hotels, grocery stores, ski rental shops, restaurants and even on the local hamburger stand. Ninety businesses now have complete computer systems and most _____ (also hook up) to an electronic mail system.

A Many police forces in Britain are facing catastrophic computer breakdowns. And several other public sector systems are on the brink of collapse, _____ (it/fear). The breakdowns threaten a repeat of disasters like the recent failure of London's ambulance network 999 service which _____ (blame) for up to 20 deaths. This breakdown was the latest example of a growing catalogue of spectacular 'hi-tech' disasters.

Disquiet about the use of computers in the public sector _____ (steadily/spread). £4 billion _____ (spend) in Britain every year on public-sector computing in a bid to improve police, hospital and government operations. But much of this cash _____ (waste) because of poor management and over-reliance on software firms to supply expertise.

C It is often said that computers have no emotions, but mine has become unbearably smug. I am no chess master but I am a fairly good amateur.

1 ☐ The machine appears to delight in the fact, diligently recording every mistake.

2 ☐ Today's super-programs are virtually unbeatable. It's a frightening statistic, 99.9 per cent of people cannot beat them. Even those who can, the grand-masters, are finding the challenge increasingly difficult.

3 ☐ Last year in Munich, Fritz 3 analysed Kasparov's moves and played the counter attack so unpredictably that Kasparov was thrown, missed a move and was, as he put it, 'slain by the silicon monster'.

So where are we in the race for artificial intelligence? Are we close to an artificial mind? In short, no. We have reached the limits of silicon-based technology.

4 ☐ There are two main hopes. The first is parallel processing which allows the computer to perform several different things at once, arriving at the end solution quicker. From this, it is hoped, neural nets will be developed – programs that learn and incorporate that learning into their behaviour.

5 ☐ The second potential technology is organic or bio-computing. Artificial neurones already exist and have been 'wired' into primitive clusters designed to replicate the pathways of the human brain. However, we still do not know enough about the brain to synthesise an organic equivalent. In many ways, of course, the computer is already our superior. It excels at storing memories of what humans have already achieved, referring to them and basing its own strategies around them (as Kasparov found to his cost), but it remains frustratingly ill-equipped to dream strategies up in the first place. In this respect we remain safe from the silicon monster.

GRAMMAR

1 Rewrite these sentences using the passive.

1 They will have to improve computer power.
   Computer power will have to be improved.

2 They need someone to take the decision for them.
   _____

3 They still have to fax the report.
   _____

4 He still has to introduce me to his boss.
   _____

5 We need someone to check the system.
   _____

6 They will have to print the document.
   _____

2 Rewrite these sentences using the passive.

1 He is afraid of a super-computer controlling humans.
   He is afraid of humans being controlled by a super-computer.

2 He doesn't like computers beating him at chess.
   _____

3 They are worried about lightning damaging the system.
   _____

4 I'd like someone to show me how this word processor works.
   _____

5 He wants someone to advise him about suitable software.
   _____

6 The authorities should take steps to control electronic espionage.
   _____

7 They must find new ways of increasing computer power.
   _____

SOUNDS

📼 Listen to the following phrases and mark the word links. Listen and check.

1 Being connected to an e-mail system is useful.
2 She's nervous about being charged too much.
3 She's looking forward to being invited over.
4 They are being contacted directly.

📼 Listen again and repeat.

LISTENING

1 **You are going to hear a man and a woman discussing the effects of computers on our ability to think. Before you listen look at the statements below and tick (✓) those which support the idea that computers decrease our ability to think and put a cross (x) by those which are against this view.**

1 The pocket calculator has reduced our ability to do mental arithmetic.
2 The pocket calculator is a great time-saver and gives people time to do more interesting tasks.
3 People who learn to write on a computer with a spellcheck can't spell properly.
4 People who can't spell won't be penalised any more.
5 The level of culture will deteriorate because the software programmers will become the main reference.
6 Humans will always be needed to program computers.

2 📼 Listen to the discussion and match the views in activity 1 with the speakers. Put W next to the views of the woman and M next to the views of the man.

3 📼 Listen again and complete the gaps in the sentences from the conversation.
1 It has destroyed _____ of a whole generation to do simple maths.
2 That's ridiculous! It's just a _____.
3 Just imagine a teacher who can't spell or
_____.
4 We won't be judging people on the way they write but _____.
5 Already children spend more time _____
_____ and less time in books.
6 Computers will never replace _____
_____.

WRITING

1 Write a paragraph summarising the views of the speakers in *Listening* activity 2.

_____
_____
_____
_____
_____
_____

2 Write a composition with the title *Have computers reduced our ability to think?* expressing your views on the topic in *Listening*.

_____
_____
_____
_____
_____
_____
_____

14 | Lifestyles

VOCABULARY

1 Put these words under the headings: *religion* or *cultural identity*.

custom ancestor baptism discrimination ethnic minority hymn dialect beliefs faith stereotype worship services ritual prayers traditions ceremonies folklore spiritual community heritage prejudice costume church

religion   **cultural identity**

_____
_____
_____
_____
_____

2 Complete this passage with words from the list in activity 1.

The Amish, who live in small, close-knit communities, are a very pious people. Their Protestant _____ came from Europe in the sixteenth century and they have managed to preserve their _____ and unique way of life. Religion is all important in their daily life and _____ are said before meals, and Sunday _____, which takes place in their homes, brings the whole community together. Amish children are not expected to marry outside the _____.

3 Choose five other words from the list in activity 1 and write sentences.

1 _____
2 _____
3 _____
4 _____
5 _____

4 Underline the words and expressions below which you can use to describe people and circle those you can use to describe places. Choose five words and write definitions using a relative clause.

laid-back anti-conformist racist popular peaceful isolated materialistic cosmopolitan

Someone who is laid-back is easygoing and relaxed.

1 _____
2 _____
3 _____
4 _____
5 _____

SOUNDS

Listen to the passage in *Vocabulary* activity 2 and mark the word links.

READING

1 Read the passage about the Argentine Pampa and choose the best title.

1 A lonely life
2 The vast Argentine Pampa
3 Where hospitality is a way of life
4 The last frontier

2 Write down six facts about the Argentine Pampa.

1 _____
2 _____
3 _____
4 _____
5 _____
6 _____

A region devoted mainly to stock-breeding and farming, the vast Argentine Pampa is a land of welcome **1** ☐ There are few towns in this vast 600-square-kilometre plain, **2** ☐ for travellers wishing to cross it, roughly equivalent to a journey between Amsterdam and Vienna. It is a land of hamlets and isolated farms, and the hospitality offered there is special, if not unique.

For the gauchos, the cowboys of the Pampa **3** ☐ the arrival of a relative, a friend or a stranger used to be regarded as an event. In our time, trains, aircraft and highways have partly put an end to this isolation, but customs have not changed for all that, and the people of the Pampa continue to offer a hospitality **4** ☐ Travellers **5** ☐ find themselves almost immediately in an ocean of land before an ever-receding horizon. Awed by a feeling of immense space and solitude, they advance along an unending road as straight as an arrow. If they cross the dry Pampa in the west they will be accompanied by the phosphorescent glow from the skeletons of animals **6** ☐ In the humid Pampa of the east they will see, on either side

of the road, behind barbed wire, hundreds of peacefully grazing animals or huge water tanks beside which horses patiently wait their turn to drink.

Travellers accustomed to short distances are sure to have forgotten something: spare parts for the car, food, a map, matches or a torch. More alarmingly, they may run out of petrol. Vehicles abandoned by the roadside are a common sight. Their owners will have to walk for hours or perhaps days before reaching an inhabited area. It is in such situations that, weary, thirsty and alone, a traveller really appreciates the generous hospitality of the Pampa.

In the Pampa, visitors have been known to receive hospitality for months and indeed years. Some have taken advantage of this to discover the region, obtain work and set up a home after sending for their families. In this old farm building or that luxurious estancia there will be a room reserved for the guest **7** ☐ No one will move into it permanently for at any time the friend of yesteryear may come back. The people of the Pampa are still waiting for him with open arms.

3 Decide where these relative clauses go in the passage.

a ... who set out from Buenos Aires or Montevideo ...

b ... that has ceased to exist in the towns.

c ... which is larger than France and, ...

d ... who lived in it for years and promised to return.

e ... whose nearest neighbours are sometimes several hundred kilometres away, ...

f ... where the practice of hospitality introduced by the Spanish is a way of life.

g ... that have succumbed to thirst, hunger or the fury of a puma.

GRAMMAR

1 Put a tick (✓) by the sentences with a defining relative clause and a cross (x) by those with a non-defining relative clause.

1 The people of the Pampa continue to offer a hospitality that has ceased to exist in the towns.

2 There are few towns in the vast 600-square-kilometre plain, which is larger than France.

3 The traveller who sets out from Buenos Aires finds himself in an ocean of land.

4 The huge herds of cattle which graze throughout the vast eastern plains are bred for meat and exported all over the world.

5 It is a land where the practice of hospitality is a way of life.

6 Our friends, who come from the south, are staying with us for a week.

7 For the gauchos, whose nearest neighbours are sometimes several hundred kilometres away, the arrival of a visitor used to be regarded as an event.

2 Underline the person or thing or clause which the relative pronoun refers to in the sentences below.

1 You will see animals that have died of thirst.

2 They are farmers who are accustomed to the lonely life of the Pampa.

3 They live in very isolated places which makes life difficult for the children who are taught to read and write by their mothers.

4 The community is very close-knit which can be both an advantage and a disadvantage.

5 They live in a region where cattle breeding is the main means of making a living.

6 Most of the people who come here want to know more about their ancestors.

7 The children get little experience of life outside the community, which is a means of preserving the traditional way of life.

3 Underline the relative pronouns which can be left out. You may need to add a preposition.

1 The household that we visited consisted of eight people.

2 We went to the dining room where everyone sang hymns.

3 The people who we met on the trip are coming to stay next weekend.

4 The gaucho, whose ranch we stayed at, was an elderly man who lived alone with his son.

5 The motel where we stayed was on the freeway out of town.

6 The community, which first came to America in the sixteenth century, lives in relative isolation.

7 The restaurant where we ate in the evening is downtown.

4 Rewrite the sentences in activity 3 leaving out the relative pronouns.

1 _____

2 _____

3 _____

4 _____

5 Look at these sentences from the passage and underline the participle clauses. Rewrite them using a relative clause.

1 A region devoted mainly to stock-breeding, ...

_____

2 ... the practice of hospitality introduced by the Spanish ...

_____

3 ... for travellers wishing to cross it ...

_____

4 ... and the hospitality offered there is special, if not unique.

_____

5 Travellers accustomed to short distances are sure to have forgotten something ...

_____

6 Vehicles abandoned by the roadside are a common sight.

_____

7 ... there will be a room reserved for the guest ...

_____

6 Rewrite these sentences using participle clauses.

1 There is a youth club for local children who are interested in sport.

_____

_____

2 The man who works in the museum comes from California.

_____

_____

3 Cattle which graze on the plains are a common sight.

_____

_____

4 The food which is served there is very special.

_____

_____

5 People who want to have a good time are advised to go downtown.

_____

_____

6 The country which accepts the most immigrants is the USA.

_____

_____

LISTENING

1 🔊 Listen to an interview with Mary-Ann. Answer the questions.

1 Where is Mary-Ann's home today?

_____

2 Where did her family come from originally?

_____

3 When did they emigrate?

_____

4 Why did they emigrate?

_____

2 🔊 Listen to the interview again. Look at the sentences below and complete them by writing one or more words in the spaces.

1 _____ per cent of the population of Cedar Rapids are of _____ origin.

2 Mary Ann works as manager of _____.

3 Her grandparents were attracted to America by _____.

4 She brings her children up with _____.

5 They maintain their traditions by holding _____.

3 Is the community discussed in the interview losing its sense of identity or is it managing to retain it?

WRITING

1 Write a short summary of the interview in *Listening*.

_____

_____

_____

_____

_____

_____

_____

2 Look back at the passage in *Vocabulary* activity 2 and write a similar passage about either an ethnic group or a religious community that you are familiar with. Try to include words from *Vocabulary* activity 1 and relative clauses.

_____

_____

_____

_____

15 | *Lucky escapes*

VOCABULARY

1 **How would you feel in the situations below. Choose a suitable word or words from the list.**

peculiar eccentric enigmatic fed-up thrilled
upset hilarious unconcerned resigned
unperturbed nervous enraged touched
baffled irritating frustrated amazed far-fetched
panic-stricken intrigued pathetic rude
thoughtful disbelieving reluctant incredulous

1 The lift you are in breaks down between floors.

_____

2 You unexpectedly receive a letter from someone claiming to be your half-brother.

_____

3 You have invited friends to a picnic and it starts to rain very heavily.

_____

4 You arrive home to find your flat has been burgled.

_____

5 You have been stuck in a traffic jam for the last two hours.

_____

6 Your friends have laid on a surprise party for your 30th birthday.

_____

2 **Choose a word or words from the list above to describe these people's behaviour or attitude.**

1 someone who taps impatiently on the table opposite you

_____

2 someone who blows cigarette smoke into your face

_____

3 someone who makes others laugh

_____

4 someone who always remembers other people's birthdays

_____

5 someone whose behaviour is difficult to understand

_____

6 someone who doesn't behave like other people

_____

READING

1 **Read the first part of the story and tick (✓) the sentence below which best summarises it.**
1 Two friends are in a lift which breaks down.
2 Two strangers are desperately trying to get out of a lift which has broken down.
3 Two strangers are having a conversation while they're waiting for the lift.
4 Two strangers are stuck in a lift waiting to be rescued.

2 **How did the writer feel when:**
1 he saw the date on his watch?
2 he saw the young businessman?
3 the businessman first started to talk?
4 the lift arrived?

3 **Underline the words and expressions which describe the other man's attitude.**

4 **Imagine you are the the writer, waiting for the lift with the other man. Write sentences expressing your wishes or regrets.**
1 not be/fortieth birthday
   I wish it wasn't my fortieth birthday.
2 be/at home with family

_____

3 the man/not start a conversation

_____

4 the lift/arrive more quickly

_____

5 not take/the lift, walk down/the stairs

_____

I t was midday exactly as I left my room and walked towards the lift on the thirty-second floor of my hotel. It was hot and sticky and I begain to miss the air conditioning in my room. I pressed the button to call the lift and waited. I looked at my watch again, but on this occasion it wasn't the time that I noticed, but the date: 3 May – my fortieth birthday – and once again I thought with a mixture of nostalgia and melancholy about life, work, family, being away from home and getting older.

I must have sighed rather loudly because when the man came up behind me, he smiled at me kindly as if he was concerned about me, even though we hadn't met. I had seen him around the hotel, a well-dressed businessman in his late twenties, at the start of his career, just beginning to make his mark. I suppose I felt mildly envious of him.

I pressed the lift button again. The man standing beside me must have read my mind. 'It certainly takes its time.' he said cheerfully. 'It certainly does,' I agreed, but something about him made me unwilling to continue the conversation.

He laughed. 'It's rather ironic, actually,' he continued and paused. This was a statement which required a response if I was not to appear rude. I turned to him and nodded. He was in a suit and tie, and he was carrying a briefcase. He looked confident and relaxed. 'I've just been reading a story about two men who get stuck in a lift,' he said.

'Is that so?' I said.

'It's called You and I are about to die, by Bill Bryson. Yes, the lift breaks down. And one of the men starts talking and tells the other man about everything that keeps going wrong in his life.' The bell sounded and the lift arrived. The doors opened. The man waited politely to let me enter first. I hesitated, then we both got in the lift.

GRAMMAR

1 Turn to page 91 and read the second part of the story. Find out what happens.

2 Complete the sentences with a few words.

1 The man continued talking while _____ _____.

2 The writer watched _____ _____.

3 When the lift stopped, the writer _____ _____.

4 He thought it was ridiculous _____ _____.

5 He only pretended _____ _____.

6 He really wanted to be _____ _____.

7 When he doors opened, there was _____ _____.

8 The woman wanted to know_____ _____.

9 The businessman replied_____ _____ _____.

10 When the doors closed_____ _____.

3 Complete these sentences in the third conditional.

1 If the writer had left his room later, he _____ _____.

2 If the lift had arrived more quickly, _____ _____.

3 If the lift hadn't stopped, _____ _____.

4 If the writer had been at home, _____ _____.

5 If the lift had been going up, _____ _____.

6 If the lift had got stuck, _____ _____.

4 Write sentences about yourself in the third conditional.

1 If I had _____

_____ .

2 I wouldn't have _____

_____ .

3 I would have _____

_____ .

4 If I hadn't _____

_____ .

5 I might have _____

_____ .

6 I could have _____

_____ .

5 Put a tick (✓) by the sentences which express regret and a cross (x) by those which express wishes.

1 I wish I could help you.
2 I wish I hadn't met them at the station.
3 I wish I knew where we were going.
4 We shouldn't have spent so long on that question.
5 I wish I had started work earlier.
6 I wish I could speak more languages.

6 Write sentences about things you regret in the past.

1 I wish I had _____

_____ .

2 I wish I hadn't _____

_____ .

3 I should have _____

_____ .

4 I shouldn't have _____

_____ .

7 Write down four things you wish you could do.

1 _____

_____

2 _____

_____

3 _____

_____

4 _____

_____

SOUNDS

1 🔊 Listen and repeat these words with two or more consonants.

ecstatic   inspired   thrilled   frustrated   partner
cracked   expected   baffled   burgled   puncture

2 What do the following words have in common?

windscreen   clipboard   handbag   seatbelt
countdown   football   postcard   setback

🔊 Listen and underline the silent letters. Say the words aloud.

3 🔊 Listen and put a tick (✓) by the words in which you can hear the underlined /r/.

purse   surprise   forgotten   hurtled   forward
care   her   nervous   unperturbed   worse

🔊 Listen again and repeat.

READING

1 Read the third and last part of the story and put a tick (✓) by the statements which are true.

1 The writer was panic-stricken.
2 The writer wanted to know the end of the story.
3 The lift continued its journey.
4 The businessman refused to tell him how the story ended.
5 They arrived safely and the businessman left the hotel.

2 Answer these questions.

1 'What happened at the end?'
   At the end of what?
2 'He begins the countdown...'
   The countdown to what?
3 I watched the floor numbers change as he spoke.
   Why are the number changing?
4 My phone and fax number's on it.
   On what?
5 You never know when you'll need one.
   One what?

I turned to the man and said, 'So tell me. What happened at the end?'

The man smiled. 'He begins the countdown, you know, nine ... eight ... seven ...'

I watched the floor numbers change as he spoke.

'And then – nothing.'

'What do you mean, nothing?'

'Nothing! The bomb doesn't go off. The man says, "You see? Nothing goes right any more." And that's it. End of story.'

The lift stopped again, and the doors opened. We walked out into the hotel lobby, which was busy but cool and breezy with air conditioning.

'You're right. It's a great story. Tell me,' I said, 'what do you do?'

'I sell life assurance policies. For those events you can never predict. Life's way of keeping you on your toes, you know.'

He felt inside his jacket. 'Here, take my card. Maybe I can interest you in a policy. Why, something might happen to you today! Run down by a truck. Taken ill with a heart attack.'

'Or get stuck in a lift with a stranger.'

He grinned. 'My phone and fax number's on it. Get in touch if you want a new life assurance policy. You never know when you'll need one. See you.' He waved and walked out into the street.

WRITING

1 Can you think of a different ending to the story? Write a few lines saying what might have happened.

_____

_____

_____

_____

_____

_____

_____

_____

_____

2 Can you think of situations in which you have behaved in a manner you later regretted? Write a few lines describing your behaviour and what you regret.

_____

_____

_____

_____

_____

_____

_____

_____

_____

_____

_____

16 | *All-time greats*

VOCABULARY

1 Complete the sentences with the correct adverbial particle from the list below.

away   across   in   for   down   up   up with   on

1   Don't forget to stand _____ when she comes _____.

2   We spent ages looking _____ a decent jazz club and we finally came _____ a great place on Fifth Avenue.

3   He never learned to read music, he just picked it _____ as he played.

4   He was playing too fast so we told him to slow _____.

5   She didn't like the song so she tore it _____ and threw it _____.

6   That's great, carry _____ playing.

7   They separated because they didn't get _____ well together.

8   She will have to put _____ her present job until she finds a better one.

2 What phrasal verbs have similar meanings to the verbs or verbal phrases in *italics*? Choose the verb from Box A and the particle from Box B and rewrite the sentences.

1   She *increased* the volume because they couldn't hear properly.
She turned the volume up because they couldn't hear properly.

2   The new song *became popular* very quickly.
_____
_____

3   He *refused* the offer.
_____
_____

4   He *noted* the lyrics on a piece of paper.
_____
_____

5   She *introduced* the problem immediately so they would have time to *discuss* it thoroughly.
_____
_____

6   He *started* playing the clarinet when he was ten.
_____
_____

7   The musical revolution of rock and roll *occurred* in the late fifties.
_____
_____

8   She *extinguished* the lights before leaving the room.
_____
_____

9   Please *take a seat.*
_____
_____

10   The song *was released* as a single.
_____
_____

A	B
take come bring	on off up out
catch write turn	about back
talk sit put get	down over across

GRAMMAR

1 Underline the phrasal verbs in the sentences below. What *type* do they belong to? Look at the *Grammar* box in your Student's Book. Write Type 1, 2, 3 or 4 by the appropriate sentences.

1   We have been looking for a new saxophonist.

2   I'm afraid you'll have to put up with the noise until the party's over.

3   I listened to their new CD this morning.

4   I came back as soon as I got your message.

5   We've turned the heater off because it's too hot in here.

6 Sit down for a few minutes.

7 Now you've got this far you'll have to go through with the show.

8 Can you pick that book up, please?

2 What type are these phrasal verbs? Write a sentence for each one.

look at   take over   carry on   hand over

pay back   get on with   put away   get over

1 _____

2 _____

3 _____

4 _____

5 _____

6 _____

7 _____

8 _____

3 Rewrite these sentences replacing the noun object with a pronoun.

1 He wrote down the lyrics.

He wrote them down.

2 He handed over the guitar.

_____

3 He did away with the vocals on the disk.

_____

4 He gave up smoking.

_____

5 She asked for a pen.

_____

6 He put the records away.

_____

7 The recording company turned down the proposal.

_____

8 I've been thinking carefully about the new show.

_____

READING

1 The two passages on page 64 are about street music. Passage A is about traditional street music. Passage B is about rap. Write down words and phrases which you could use to talk about these types of music.

Passage A

_____

_____

Passage B

_____

_____

2 Which passages do you think the sentences below are likely to be from?

1 But in fact who does still remember these old songs now, if not some inner voice or this anachronistic street musician?

2 Shut up in a club, street music loses its special identity.

3 Sometimes someone even stops to put a coin in the cup fixed to the barrel-organ.

4 Street music can never really be replicated, for it is a spontaneous art form.

5 A sound system would be set up on the pavement or maybe in the window of an apartment.

6 For the old street-songs are part of its soul.

3 Read the passages and check your answers to activity 2.

4 Answer these questions about passage A.

1 He is below my window, ...
  Who is below the window?

2 ... singing along with the choruses, ...
  What part of the songs is he likely to know?

3 ... another perforated strip in the machine ...
  What machine?

4 ... a culture attacked on every side by ...
  What culture?

5 Read passage B and decide if these statements are true or false.

   1 Rap music originated in the Caribbean.

   2 It developed on the streets of New York before it became well-known.

   3 It started to lose its special identity from the moment it was recorded.

   4 True rap, like any form of street music, can only be found on the street.

6 Underline all the phrasal verbs in the passages.

7 Which phrasal verbs in the passages are similar in meaning to:

   be preoccupied with   keep going   install   hold   go in the direction of   imprison   continue

A **He is below my window now, at noon.** He takes up his pitch at the crossroads in the sunlight, cranks the handle of his barrel-organ and sings the songs of old Paris, songs of the people and love affairs that go wrong. I find myself almost unconsciously singing along with the choruses, as if I had always known them. But in fact who does still remember these old songs now, if not some inner voice or this anachronistic street musician?

Down there on the pavement, people are wrapped up in their own problems. Few stop. Some smile as they pass by; others walk on with their heads down, scowling. The singer is not bothered. He just puts another perforated strip in the machine and goes on singing. Cars pass, office workers head for lunch, gangs of children form and disperse. Sometimes someone even stops to put a coin in the cup fixed to the barrel-organ.

The street musician is keeping alive a culture attacked on every side by the modern world. His long hair and red scarf, the scruffy cap pulled down over one eye, may look like fancy dress, but they are really a way of letting passers-by know that Paris belongs to the people who live in it. For the old street-songs are part of its soul. And that soul will never die as long as the melodies of the past can still be heard.

B **Perhaps the best known authentic modern street music is rap** which was born in New York and heavily influenced by Caribbean musical traditions. Like other musicians before them, rappers developed their art in the street before they had access to production facilities and commercial outlets. In the Bronx and Harlem, the first rappers began in the mid-70s to put on 'block-parties' in the streets for the inhabitants of blocks of flats. A sound system would be set up on the pavement or maybe in the window of an apartment.

Shut up in a club, street music loses its special identity. In a recording studio, even when simply relayed by microphone, it has to pass through electronic devices, which rob it of some of its vitality. Street music can never really be replicated, for it is a spontaneous art form. It is inseparable from everything that is going on around it at the time of its creation. It needs space.

LISTENING

1 You are going to hear an interview with a musician in a symphony orchestra. Complete the gaps with appropriate question words.

☐ _____ did you choose the violin?

☐ _____ did you first study music?

☐ _____ have you been in the orchestra?

☐ _____ do you rehearse?

☐ _____ were you when you started to play?

☐ _____ musicians are there?

☐ _____ other instruments do you play?

2 🔊 Listen and number the questions in activity 1 in the order you hear them.

3 🔊 Listen again. Answer the questions from activity 1. Write your answers in the third person.

1 _____

2 _____

3 _____

4 _____

5 _____

6 _____

SOUNDS

1 🔊 Listen and mark the word links.

1 He wrote it down.

2 She looked at him.

3 They came up with it.

4 He turned them down.

5 We will have to put up with it.

6 I threw it away.

Say the sentences aloud.

2 Put the words below into groups according to how you pronounce the letters 'ch'.

choir   charts   orchestra   beach   scratch   chord
pitch   anachronistic   lunch   chorus

/k/ _____

_____

/tʃ/ _____

_____

🔊 Listen and check.

WRITING

Is there a tradition of street music in your country? What sort of music it is? What are the origins of this music? Write a paragraph describing it.

_____

_____

_____

_____

_____

_____

_____

_____

_____

_____

_____

_____

_____

_____

_____

_____

_____

_____

_____

VOCABULARY AND GRAMMAR

1 Match the containers with the things you would expect to buy in them.

can	potatoes
carton	crisps
sack	wine
bottle	toothpaste
box	soup
jar	jam
packet	cream
tube	matches

2 Circle the odd-one-out. Write a sentence giving your reason.

1 money aluminium silver iron gold
Money is the odd-one-out because it is the only one that isn't the name of a metal.

2 nylon furniture iron wood glass
_____

3 butter beer cheese yogurt cream
_____

4 newspaper packet box bowl basket
_____

5 bottle bucket mug sack jug
_____

6 heap pile bit drop piece
_____

3 Match the food with the amounts.

a slice		milk
a piece		bacon
a pinch	of	bread
a litre		cake
a rasher		salt

4 Underline the uncountable words in the list below.

newspaper box furniture toothpaste journey rubbish trousers bucket fun present money symphony weather job music research news medicine diet advice item accommodation information

5 Complete the sentences with words from the list in activity 4.

1 Her house is full of beautiful, antique

_____.

2 We're going to the south coast so I've sent off for a holiday _____ brochure.

3 I haven't had any _____ from them since they left.

4 A lot of people write letters to the _____ column of the magazine.

5 The children had such _____ at the playgroup that they'll be going again on Saturday.

6 Scientists are collecting _____ in order to improve _____ forecasting techniques.

6 Write sentences with five uncountable nouns from the list in activity 4.

1 _____
2 _____
3 _____
4 _____
5 _____

READING

1 Read *Tips from a mean millionaire* and choose the best definition for the word *tightwadding*.

1 being imaginatively mean

2 saving as much as possible

3 living on bare essentials

Tips from a mean millionaire

Amy Dacyczyn, the founder of *The Tightwad Gazette* – a monthly newsletter promoting thrift as a viable alternative lifestyle – is making tea. In her kitchen in rural Maine she boils the kettle, pours the excess water into a Thermos, so she won't have to waste electricity boiling more later, then opens her elderly fridge to get the milk. She has a husband, six children and an income of over half a million dollars each year, but all the fridge contains are three old glass apple juice bottles full of milk, a weary-looking Tupperware box, a few covered bowls of leftovers and an apple with a few bites out of it.

Welcome to the world of tightwadding, where super-creative hyper-frugality is the order of the day, nothing is ever bought new if it can humanly be found second hand, ordinary shops are visited only for special offers that extensive prior research has proved to be the very cheapest available.

Amy Dacyczyn is a multi-millionaire, but if you saw her on the street – or diving into a skip for some discarded bargain – you certainly wouldn't guess it. She has got rich by being imaginatively mean. Her monthly food bill is $180. Her yearly budget to clothe the children never exceeds $50. And it is her *Tightwad Gazette*, to which over 100,000 Americans have subscribed at $12 a year, and in which she imparts frugal hints, that has made her wealthy.

When Amy got married, she and her husband Jim decided that there were three things they wanted more than anything else: a large family, a business they could run from home and a farmhouse. But their combined salaries could barely cover essentials. They decided they would have to be ruthless about cutting costs if they wanted to achieve their goals.

First they divided all their expenses into essentials and optionals and cut out every optional: meals out, cigarettes and alcohol, magazines, junk food, new clothes. Then they looked at how they could pare down the essentials: utilities, groceries, petrol. Within seven years they had saved $49,000.

Everything about Amy reflects the tightwad life. Her hair has been washed in cheap, bulk-bought shampoo and she is wearing minimal make-up. Since she is dedicated to frugality with time as well as money, her maroon blouse is unironed. The jeans were bought in a sale. Her sneakers have a three-year plan all their own. Today she's wearing this year's pair; last year's pair she wears when she's not seeing visitors and the year before's she wears around the garden. All come from sales, at a maximum $15 a pair.

The issue of surplus money is the core of tightwaddery. There's no point in scrimping in one area if you're wasting money in another and still not achieving the quality of life you really want. And the tightwad life is not only about spending less but spending in a way that reflects your values.

2 Underline the uncountable nouns in the passage.

3 Write down four ways in which Amy saves money.

She uses a Thermos to keep water hot in order to save electricity.

1 _____

2 _____

3 _____

4 _____

4 Write down six things which Amy considers as optionals.

1 _____
2 _____
3 _____
4 _____
5 _____
6 _____

5 Find words in the box which mean the same as:

1	tired	6	heart
2	excess	7	without pity
3	cut	8	spend the strict minimum
4	frugal	9	possible
5	odd bits of food	10	previous

```
ruthless   core   viable   thrifty   pare down
prior   scrimp   leftovers   weary   surplus
```

WRITING

1 Look back at the optionals you noted in *Reading* activity 4. Write sentences saying which of these things you could/couldn't do without.

_____

_____

_____

_____

_____

_____

_____

_____

_____

_____

_____

2 Imagine you need to save money for a particular purpose. Write a few lines explaining what you would do. What would you be prepared to give up?

_____

_____

_____

_____

_____

_____

_____

_____

_____

_____

LISTENING AND VOCABULARY

1 🔲 Listen to four conversations. Put the number of the conversation by what the speakers are enquiring about or asking for.

bank loans ☐   pension ☐

unemployment benefit ☐   borrowing cash ☐

exchanging foreign currency ☐   cash cards ☐

2 🔲 Listen again and complete the information.

1   Don't take too much out because the
_____ will be _____.
Then, we won't have to worry about the
_____ instalment on the fifteenth.

2   Have you got an account with our
_____?
What are the _____ rates on short-
term _____ at the moment?

3   I have a savings account with your
_____.
Cash _____ and balance enquiries
can be carried out at any machine ...

4   Could you tell me what the _____
is, please?
It's often a good idea to take a few
_____ with you ...

SOUNDS

Look at the sentences below. Underline the words you think the speaker will link.

1   We've had a great deal of trouble lately.
2   Can you lend me some cash, please?
3   It's made of glass.
4   I'll draw some money out tonight.

🔲 Listen and check. Say the sentences aloud.

GRAMMAR

1 Complete the sentences with *few, a few, little* or *a little*.

1   Unfortunately we made _____ new
friends when we were in Italy.

2   I paid very _____ income tax last year.

3   Would you like some more pasta? Only
_____, please.

4   There are very _____ building societies
in this area.

5   There's only _____ cheese left.

6   Could you lend me _____ dollars,
please?

2 Complete the sentences with a suitable quantity word. Choose from the list below.

hardly any   enough   several   any   much
a great deal of   some

1   Be careful, there is _____ money left in
your deposit account.

2   I had to pay _____ income tax last year,
so I'm broke now.

3   She tried _____ pairs of shoes on before
choosing the black ones.

4   I'm afraid I haven't _____ time to read
the document now.

5   I wish I didn't have to pay so _____
VAT.

6   Would you like _____ more tea?

7   Did you have _____ trouble getting
through Customs?

READING

1 Look at the passage on page 71 and decide which sentence best summarises the main idea.

1 It is difficult to keep up with new technology.

2 Things that appear modern today quickly become either commonplace or out of date.

3 Most new gadgets only last a short time on the market.

4 New technology leads to a better world.

2 Match these headings with the different sections (1 to 4) of the passage.

Intelligent clothes   Animal spare parts

Smart money   Interactive TV

3 Read the passage and check. Underline the successful gadgets it mentions and circle things that never became popular.

4 Answer the questions.

1 *Which proves, if nothing else, that predicting the future is not a game to take lightly.* What does *which* refer to?

_____

_____

2 What is the main advantage of the smart cashcards?

_____

_____

3 Why are these clothes described as 'intelligent'?

_____

_____

4 Who is likely to be interested in intelligent clothes?

_____

_____

5 *... and active participation, which we associate with the box.*

What does *the box* refer to?

_____

_____

6 In what way will viewers of this type of TV be more active?

_____

_____

7 In what area of science are these transgenic animals likely to be most useful?

_____

_____

5 Do you agree with the writer's choice of what will be big in the next decade? Write down a few more things that you think will become commonplace.

_____

_____

Ten years ago huge-brained personal computers, CD players, satellite dishes and microwaves were available but hardly commonplace. Most of us were only thinking about them rather than buying them. Now, of course, if we don't have them, there has to be a reason why. Nothing at first seems so revolutionary as the Latest Advance; and nothing becomes mundane so quickly. And in the past 30 years, Latest Advances have been coming at us faster and more furiously than at any time in history.

Go back 20 years and you are virtually in the Stone Age. The Latest Advances in 1974 were the pocket calculator, the home food freezer and credit cards. And these were the successes. At about the same time, quadrophonic discs, the Wankel rotary engine and a diet made from processed soya beans were also being tipped as the coming things. Which proves, if nothing else, that predicting the future is not a game to take lightly.

But let's be brave. What's going to be big in the next ten years? It's always tempting to believe that surely, this time, we've reached some sort of plateau and there won't be any new technology, new gizmos to contend with; that things will stay as they are for a bit longer. But yesterday's Latest Advances are already being pushed aside to make way for an even better world.

1 _____

Banks and telecommunications networks are working on new systems to replace old-fashioned notes and coins with smart cashcards. You will be able to fill your smart cards with money, either by swiping them through a cashpoint machine, or through a telephone terminal dialled through to your bank account.

You simply present your card to the retailer, restaurateur or whoever, who swipes the card through a reader and credits himself with the same number of blips that he takes off you. When he wants to bank his takings he swipes his card through the reading machine and loads up with the credits he's taken since the last swipe. There will be no need to go through a central processing agency to get at the money.

2 _____

By cooling your armpits, backbone, groin and breastbone it is possible to stimulate resistant fat cells and burn more calories. For dieters and fitness fanatics, intelligent thermo-regulatory clothing will keep parts of the body cool, while keeping the rest of the body warm. You won't just lose weight. Champions of intelligent clothing claim that judiciously stimulating your coolness will also perk up your circulation, boost your immune system and regulate the production of hormones.

3 _____

What will it offer? A mix of anything from home shopping (where you walk through a shop, choosing items on the way), to mind-boggling quiz games, and sports events. The viewer will be able to freeze-frame, select different camera angles and watch the same sequences over and over again. Interactive TV promises to put an end to the distinction between passive watching and active participation, which we associate with the box.

4 _____

A bull in the Netherlands called Herman can now breed female offspring with a modified gene that enables them to produce human milk protein. There are pigs in Britain with human lungs and hearts. In other words, the divisions between men and beasts are being blurred, and transgenic animals, as these hybrids are known, could hold the key to an entirely new kind of medicine. Some people are already postulating a future in which herds of transgenic animals will be kept ready to supply human proteins, antibodies and organs for transplant operations.

GRAMMAR

1 Look back at the passage and complete these sentences with the future perfect or the future continuous form of the verb in brackets.

1 Ten years from now we _____ (use) all sorts of new gadgets which are not commonplace yet.

2 Smart cashcards _____ (replace) notes and coins by the end of the year 2010.

3 In a few years' time many dieters _____ (wear) thermo-regulatory clothes to help them lose weight.

4 By the end of the next decade interactive TV _____ (replace) today's TV.

5 Viewers _____ (participate) actively in many programmes rather than watching passively.

6 In a few years time, surgeons _____ (perform) transplants with animal organs.

2 Write sentences using the future continuous with the ideas you wrote down in *Reading* activity 5.

_____

_____

_____

_____

3 Write sentences about things that you hope you will accomplish in your professional life. Think about:

earnings   travel   responsibility   interest

Ten years from now I hope I will be
earning a good salary.

_____

_____

_____

_____

_____

_____

_____

_____

4 Write sentences about things you hope you will have accomplished when you are very old. Think about:

family   house   travel   health   friends

I hope I will have travelled to many
foreign countries.

_____

_____

_____

_____

_____

_____

_____

_____

SOUNDS

🔲 Listen and tick (✓) when you hear the underlined 't' or 'd'.

1 You won't just lose weight.

2 Old-fashioned notes.

3 credit card

4 cashpoint machine

5 the best part of 25 years

LISTENING

1 🔲 Listen to a report on the world situation in the second half of the 19th century. Number the issues the speaker mentions in the correct order.

famine ☐

population ☐

energy resources ☐

environment ☐

war ☐

Is the speaker generally optimistic or pessimistic about the future?

_____

_____

2 🔲 Listen again and decide whether these statements are true or false.

1 Family planning schemes have prevented a population explosion in many developing countries.

2 By the year 2025, the world population will not have increased dramatically.

3 A demographic explosion is likely to result in the deterioration of the environment.

4 Crop growing is likely to become a major problem.

5 Energy resources will probably determine the balance of power in the future.

6 Over the last twenty years, new sources of clean energy have gradually replaced oil and nuclear power.

7 Many rich countries do not finance energy research projects because they are too costly.

3 Rewrite the sentences which are false.

1 _____

2 _____

3 _____

4 _____

4 Write sentences saying what you think the world situation is likely to be in twenty years. Look back at the issues in activity 1. Try to use the future perfect where appropriate.

_____

WRITING

Write a few lines expressing your predictions for the issues in *Listening* activity 2 and stating your reasons. Are you generally optimistic or pessimistic?

_____

19 | *Legendary Britain*

VOCABULARY

1 Write down words formed from the words below. What parts of speech are they? You can use your dictionary.

believe   consider   expect   fact   know   myth
remain   think   understand

_____

_____

_____

_____

_____

_____

_____

_____

_____

_____

2 Match the definitions below with the words in the box.

curse   fact   fiction   hoax   legend   mystery
superstition   spell   omen   soul

1 imaginative story-telling
2 a sign of some future event
3 something which cannot be explained
4 a wish for evil or harm to befall someone
5 an ancient traditional story
6 a deep-rooted general belief or fear
7 the human spirit
8 a magic influence
9 a practical joke or trick played on someone
10 a piece of information

3 Choose five words from activity 2 and write sentences.

1 _____
2 _____
3 _____
4 _____
5 _____

READING AND GRAMMAR

1 Read the passage about butterfly superstitions and find out what butterflies are commonly associated with in folk-lore.

2 There are various superstitions surrounding butterflies. Some say they are lucky and some unlucky. Find three examples of each in the passage.

3 Underline all the passive constructions with the form subject + passive + *to* infinitive.

4 Rewrite the sentences you underlined using the passive construction *It* + passive + *that* clause.

_____

_____

_____

_____

_____

_____

_____

_____

_____

_____

Butterflies

Butterflies have from early times been associated with human souls. In ancient Egypt, the soul at death was thought to leave the body as the butterfly leaves the chrysalis. In Burma the *win-laik-pya*, or soul-butterfly, is believed to fly abroad when its owner sleeps, meeting the soul-butterflies of other persons and animals and returning when the sleeper wakes. Burmese children are still taught never to awaken anyone too suddenly because it is believed that if the *win-laik-pya* cannot get back in time, the person will die.

In Gaelic tradition, the newly dead were thought to be sometimes visible in the form of a butterfly hovering over the corpse. In Ireland, this was a sign of everlasting happiness for the soul. In Scotland, a golden butterfly flying over a dying person was considered to be a very good omen for his or her future welfare.

One legend tells how a soul wandered through time and space, and returned at last to the body in butterfly form. It was about to enter the man's mouth when a neighbour killed it. In the most common version of the story, the man is alleged to have died at once.

This death-and-soul connection, which protects the insect in some areas, causes it to be feared and persecuted in others. To see three together is considered unlucky, to see one flying at night is believed to be a death omen. In many parts of Britain, it is believed that the first seen in any one year should be killed, otherwise misfortune will follow. In Gloucestershire it used to be said that if the first butterfly seen in summer was a white one, the observer would eat white bread all the year. In other words the person would be prosperous and would be able to eat fine food. If it was brown, the person would only be able to afford the humbler brown bread. All along the Scottish border, red butterflies were formerly hunted because they were thought to be witches.

LISTENING

1 🔊 Listen to descriptions of six common superstitions. Put the number of the description by the object of the superstition.

- [ ] ladder
- [ ] black cat
- [ ] umbrella
- [ ] horseshoe
- [ ] bat
- [ ] mirror

2 🔊 What is considered lucky or unlucky? Listen again and complete these sentences with a few words.

1 In some places, it is a death omen if a bat flies

_____.

When bats fly about early in the evening, it is a sign of _____.

2 It is a very good sign if a black cat comes

_____.

To meet a black cat is usually thought to be fortunate, especially if it _____

_____.

3 In almost every country the horseshoe brings

_____.

If you find a horseshoe, you should take it home and _____

_____.

4 Many people, even today, carefully avoid

_____.

You can counteract bad luck by keeping your fingers crossed until _____

_____.

5 Many people believe that breaking a mirror will cause _____.

If a girl lights two candles and looks into a mirror on Hallowe'en, she will see _____

_____.

6 Most people believe that it is unlucky to _____

_____.

An umbrella unnecessarily opened during fine weather may _____.

75

3 Write two sentences using a passive construction for each superstition.

1 *Witches were said to turn themselves into bats.*

2 _____

3 _____

4 _____

5 _____

6 _____

WRITING

Are there similar superstitions surrounding these things in your country? Write a few sentences describing common superstitions from your country.

_____
_____
_____
_____
_____
_____
_____
_____

SOUNDS

1 Underline the silent letters in the following words.

sword ghosts wrecked tomb psychics sign
doubt

[cassette] Listen and check.

2 Circle the word with a different vowel sound.

1 ground drown power tower wounded
2 first earth burial return curse
3 rode omen oak stone mouth
4 stump monk move flood love

[cassette] Listen and check.

READING

1 Read the passage about The Lost Continent of Atlantis and find four theories which have been suggested to explain the disappearance of the continent.

2 Are these statements true or false?

1 Atlantis was a large island which was destroyed by an earthquake.
2 It is not possible for an earthquake to destroy a large continent.
3 Atlantis is more likely to have been destroyed by floods.
4 In the past many scientists believed that Atlantis was situated in the Atlantic Ocean.
5 Theories of continental drift suggest a geological explanation for the disappearance of Atlantis.
6 It is unlikely that Atlantis was the mythical name for North America.

3 Complete these statements with explanations from the passage.

1 Atlantis can't have been destroyed by an earthquake because _____ .

2 It can't have been submerged by flooding because _____ .

3 A volcano could not have blown it into the sea _____ .

4 Atlantis can't have been the Greek name for North America _____
_____ .

The Lost Continent of Atlantis

For centuries people have been speculating about the existence of the legendary continent of Atlantis. In Greek mythology Atlantis is described as a large island which was destroyed by an earthquake around 9,000 BC. But could an earthquake account for the sinking of a great continent such as Atlantis is believed to have been? Most scientists think it extremely unlikely. An earthquake might have destroyed part of the island continent, or caused landslides around its shores, but a quake that would have destroyed a huge landmass is unheard-of. Had Atlantis been an island with a very low profile, it might have been at least partly submerged by flooding, but Plato describes Atlantis as a mountainous country. A tidal wave might have washed over Atlantis, but it would not have washed it away. And a volcanic eruption could have blown part of the continent into the ocean, but if Atlantis had been anywhere near the size claimed by Plato, much would still be towering above the sea.

And where was Atlantis situated? Plato writes that it was in the western sea or Atlantic Ocean as it is called today. If this is correct, could there be a geological explanation for its disappearance? Before the theory of continental drift was widely accepted, many geologists supposed that a continent, Atlantis, must have occupied the present position of the Atlantic. This continent was thought to have sunk beneath the Atlantic waves. But today most scientists agree that as we push the continents back to their original places, we effectively squeeze Atlantis off the map. So could Atlantis have been North America, which, having drifted away, was thought to have been submerged in the Atlantic? No. The continents are moving apart at the rate of between one and six inches a year – hardly enough to give rise to Plato's account of the submergence of Atlantis in a day and a night.

Not surprisingly, believers in Atlantis hotly contest the findings of modern science that seek to dismiss the existence of the lost continent. If a once-derided theory such as continental drift can eventually earn the backing of the respectable scientific community, the Atlantists argue, might not other theories one day gain the same acceptance? Perhaps human beings existed long before the scientists' estimates. Perhaps there was some extraordinary global catastrophe. Perhaps Atlantis did exist after all.

GRAMMAR

1 Underline all the sentences in the passage with past modals.

2 What is the difference in meaning between these sentences?

1   a   The continent can't have been destroyed by an earthquake.

    b   The continent may not have been destroyed by an earthquake.

2   a   Scientists believe that it must have been submerged by flooding.

    b   Scientists believe that it could have been submerged by flooding.

3   a   Atlantis couldn't have existed.

    b   Atlantis might not have existed.

3 Write sentences using a past modal.

1   Perhaps human beings existed long before the scientists' estimates.

_____

2   Perhaps there was some extraordinary global catastrophe.

_____

3   Perhaps Atlantis did exist after all.

_____

4   The Greek gods were probably people who had accomplished extraordinary feats.

_____

5   It is very unlikely that the dinosaurs were destroyed by a comet hitting the Earth.

_____

6   It is unlikely that extra-terrestrial beings have visited Earth.

_____

7   It is certain that the Vikings reached North America.

_____

8   It is possible that Atlantis was a small island in the Aegean.

_____

GRAMMAR

1 **What products do you think the advertising slogans below refer to? Choose from this list.**

exercise machine   coffee   face cream
emergency medical alarm   colour film   underwear
camcorder   car   watch   air conditioning

1 The aroma is just a taste of the richness to come

2 Not all our bright ideas are under the bonnet

3 Your travelling companion in the palm of your hand

4 The link between the past and the present

5 Waist disposal unit

6 Discover moisture that absorbs instantly then hydrates all day

7 Nothing is more comfortable than Sloggi (But only just)

8 Freezing may be great for vegetables, it's not so good for Mrs Jackson ...

9 For help and security at the touch of a button

10 Now even sharper colours

Turn to page 91 and check.

2 **Write an explanation for five of the slogans in activity 1 using a suitable reporting verb.**

The slogan claims that the aroma of the coffee gives you an idea of its rich taste.

1 _____

_____

2 _____

_____

3 _____

_____

4 _____

_____

5 _____

_____

3 **Change these sentences into reported speech.**

1 'Its petrol consumption is very reasonable even at high speeds,' he claimed.

_____

_____

2 'You must come up with a new advertising campaign for the autumn, Jim,' she ordered.

_____

_____

3 'I bought an unknown brand of ketchup and the kids won't touch it,' she complained.

_____

_____

4 'I've tried it out on the children's clothes and it really works,' she said.

_____

_____

5 'What brand of washing powder do you use, madam?' he asked.

_____

_____

6 'I will stop smoking if cigarettes go up in price,' he promised.

_____

_____

7 'We might go to Madeira for the winter,' he said.

_____

_____

8 'It really does taste better than any other brands on the market,' he boasted.

_____

_____

4 Change these sentences into direct speech.

1 They told me they wanted to stay an extra night.

_____

2 He promised to be very quiet when he came in.

_____

3 She warned me there would be a speed trap on the motorway.

_____

4 He boasted about how well he knew the area.

_____

5 She advised us not to stay out too late.

_____

6 He threatened to go to the police if it happened again.

_____

7 She suggested they went out for a meal.

_____

8 He admitted he had behaved badly at the party.

_____

READING AND VOCABULARY

1 In what situations are you most likely to take notice of advertisements?

1 in public transport
2 at the cinema
3 on television
4 on the radio
5 in a magazine or newspaper
6 in your car
7 walking in the street
8 leaflets through the post

Are there situations where you do not come into contact with advertisements?

2 What was the last advertisement that you can remember for each of the situations in activity 1? Write a few words describing each advertisement.

_____

_____

_____

_____

_____

_____

3 Read the passage on page 80 and choose the best title from the list below.

1 Target audiences
2 Off the beaten track
3 And now, instead of graffiti – lavatory ads
4 Small time advertising

4 Answer the questions.

1 Why is the lavatory door 'after your soul'?

_____

2 What, according to the passage, is the major advantage of advertising in toilets?

_____

3 Why are people more likely to remember the advertisements in toilets?

_____

4 What did many people object to at first?

_____

5 Why wouldn't Seinpaal advertise sneakers in a classy restaurant?

_____

6 Where would be a better place to advertise sneakers?

_____

5 What is the target audience for the following products likely to be?

Cartier bracelet   encyclopedia

high-calorie drink   training shoes

convertible sports car   low-calorie chocolate

Ray Ban sunglasses

If you were advertising these products, where would you advertise?

JUST WHEN YOU THOUGHT you had reached a place of sanctuary, your eyes alert you to the fact that even the lavatory door you are staring at is after your soul: welcome to the wonderful world of Captive Audience/ Strategic Advertising.

'For the men's room, ads are usually above the urinals,' explains Dutch Captive Audience partner Shedrick Seinpaal. 'The first advertiser did laugh and say: "These days they don't even leave you alone in the toilet." But he bought the idea.'

Seinpaal started to develop the idea when, as a marketing analyst, he became aware that people were being bombarded with adverts to the point where they hardly remembered them.

'That's where the idea began,' he says. 'To advertise in a space where you have undivided attention. The only space I could think of was the rest rooms in public places.'

He teamed up with a US company, Strategic Advertising. Now, at stalls in 350 different outlets across the Netherlands, up to 100 advertisers peddle their wares in 'tastefully' framed adverts. The cost is 100 guilders ($62) per ad per month.

Seinpaal admits that his firm had to do a lot of educating to get the idea across, but still claims that public lavatories are the best place to advertise. He explains: 'People have between 20 seconds and three minutes of undivided attention. Also, they remember the ads because they are only in places that reach the advertisers' target audience. For example, if you want to advertise sneakers you wouldn't do that in a classy restaurant but in a disco.

'People didn't take us seriously at first,' he laughs. 'The second reaction was an objection to the idea that their business would be associated with the smells in a toilet. But as we went along, their attitude changed. When people saw where we put the framed adverts and they actually went through the motions themselves, they found there was no way not to see them.'

Captive Audience's advertisers tend to be small businesses such as hairdressers, nail boutiques, photographers and limousine services. 'It's expanding all the time. It's hard work – you have to sell very aggressively, and nobody waits for you in the advertising business.'

SOUNDS

1 How do you pronounce the following words? Put them into four groups according to the way you pronounce the underlined letter 'o'.

pr<u>o</u>mise   pr<u>o</u>mote   w<u>o</u>nder   pr<u>o</u>duct   sl<u>o</u>gan
c<u>o</u>smetics   c<u>o</u>mmercial   m<u>o</u>ney   ph<u>o</u>to   sp<u>o</u>nsor
c<u>o</u>mpany   gl<u>o</u>bal   c<u>o</u>mplain   c<u>o</u>ntroversial
b<u>o</u>nus   c<u>o</u>me   c<u>o</u>nfess   c<u>o</u>lour

/ɒ/: _____

/əʊ/: prom<u>o</u>te _____

/ə/: pr<u>o</u>mote _____

/ʌ/: _____

2 Underline the stressed syllables in the words in activity 1.

🔲 Listen and check.

VOCABULARY

1 Complete these sentences with words from *Sounds* activity 1. You may have to change the form of some of the verbs or nouns.

1 Rolls Royce, the British luxury car company, is _____ the new Bentley as a car for women.

2 Coca-Cola was the first company to use _____ advertising techniques.

3 A successful message is one which is immediately associated with the _____ it is promoting.

4 This message should avoid _____ issues if it is to be used throughout the world.

5 The first TV _____ was shown on a New York television station in 1941.

6 Today many television and radio programmes are _____ by private companies.

7 An unexpected extra is a _____.

8 Huge amounts of _____ go into choosing the brand name of a new product.

2 Write the nouns for these verbs.

Verbs	Nouns	Verbs	Nouns
advertise	_____	promise	_____
admit	_____	promote	_____
analyse	_____	suggest	_____
appeal	_____	threaten	_____
complain	_____	warn	_____

LISTENING

1 You are going to hear a woman talking about a weekend break in Paris. She explains that she saw an ad in a magazine which offered 'weekend breaks with a difference to the glamour spots of Europe'. Write down words or phrases that you would expect to find in the ad.

2 Listen to the conversation and put a tick (✓) by the things that were different from what the ad promised.

1 They flew with an unknown charter company.
2 The plane was delayed.
3 The outward flight took a long time.
4 There was no taxi service from the airport.
5 There were no car parking facilities near the hotel.
6 The hotel was in a dreadful neighbourhood.
7 The bedroom was small and dirty.
8 The room service was very slow.
9 The bedroom overlooked a brick wall.
10 The trip cost more than expected.

3 Rewrite the sentences you ticked in activity 2 saying what the advertisement promised.

1 _____
2 _____
3 _____
4 _____
5 _____
6 _____
7 _____

WRITING

1 Write the advertisement for the weekend break in Paris.

_____
_____
_____
_____
_____

2 Write a short passage about how advertising influences you and what you buy.

_____
_____
_____
_____
_____

Tapescripts

MAN Guess what? I met a woman this afternoon at the language conference who can speak nine different languages. She came from China originally and married a Frenchman who has been working for the last twenty years in consulates all over the world. She speaks English just as well as you or me. You couldn't tell she wasn't a native speaker.

WOMAN That's amazing. Doesn't she get them mixed up? Some people are so lucky, aren't they? I mean, to be gifted for learning languages. I wish I was. I learned French at school for six years, and I still can't understand a word when we go on holiday there. They don't seem to say anything I learned at school, and everyone speaks so fast. I still find it attractive. It's such a serious-sounding language.

MAN Well, at least you can understand written French, can't you? That's more than I can do. I did Spanish at school.

WOMAN How marvellous! I've always wanted to speak Spanish. I love listening to people speaking it, don't you? It's an exciting-sounding language. And so melodious. I can happily sit back and listen to it without it bothering me even though I can't understand the meaning of what they're saying. It's almost like listening to music.

MAN Yeah, yeah, I enjoyed learning it. Even school didn't put me off. And it isn't terribly difficult, either. Not like Japanese. That's incredibly hard. I had a go at that in my last year at college.

WOMAN Did you really? I am impressed!.

MAN I only did a year. I thought it might be useful in the electronics industry. But I was hopeless at it. To start with, the sounds are so strange I couldn't even repeat words properly. And as for the alphabet, it's unbelievably complicated.

WOMAN The trouble is, you have to make such an effort to learn another language, don't you? It's much harder than studying maths or history or something. Especially if you aren't gifted. It's really quite daunting. Another language that is supposed to be pretty difficult is Arabic. I'd love to be able to speak it, wouldn't you? It sounds so mysterious and exotic. But, judging from my success in French, though, there's very little point in my even trying.

MAN I'd really like to be able to speak German. It would be really useful for my work. You see, I work for a German firm now.

WOMAN Do you? You are full of surprises! Why don't you go to evening lessons?

MAN I have been thinking about it. But it's supposed to be a complicated language to learn, and I'm not sure I can cope with all the extra work. It's very different from Spanish or Japanese, so it would mean starting all over again.

WOMAN I wouldn't mind learning German as well. I'll tell you what. Let's go to classes together, shall we? It would be much more fun if we both went, and we'd be able to give each other moral support.

1 Some people are so lucky, aren't they?
2 Well, at least you can understand written French, can't you?
3 I love listening to people speaking it, don't you?
4 The trouble is, you have to make such an effort to learn another language, don't you?
5 I'd love to be able to speak it, wouldn't you?
6 Let's go to classes together, shall we?

1   Let's go on a course together, shall we?
2   You couldn't lend me your book, could you?
3   Don't be too angry with him, will you?
4   There won't be too many people, will there?
5   She looks very well, doesn't she?
6   Hold this for a moment, will you?
7   There aren't any spare cassettes, are there?
8   You can't come with me, can you?
9   You haven't been to the States, have you?
10 There isn't anyone at the office today, is there?

frown	bow
stare	bear
born	yawn
though	blow
warm	form
put	foot
laugh	arm

SPEAKER 1 Um, I was the middle child in the family – I think that's probably the most difficult position to be in. Er, you always feel left out. I was never spoilt like the youngest child, and I didn't get my parents' full attention like the eldest. Um, however, that did give me sort of freedom 'cause I was left to my own devices. Um, I was three, just three when, um, my little brother came along, and I, I really resented him – I was quite jealous. I used to pinch him. Um, I suppose it was just a way of, er, trying to draw attention to me, but, it, it only made things worse and it got me into trouble. My older sister who was, um, five years older than me, so she wasn't really interested in me.

SPEAKER 2 I think I was very privileged really, because I had a wonderful relationship with my parents. Um, they lavished all their time and energy on me. Um, I don't think I suffered because I did have a lot of friends. Um, I didn't envy my friends who had horrid little brothers and sisters who broke their belongings. Oh, I was a bit spoilt, I suppose – it's inevitable. But that made me very self-sufficient which is a great advantage for later life. Er, the problem is, it does make you selfish, because you are used to all the attention. I used to dream of having a baby brother or sister, but it was only because it appealed to me as some sort of game.

SPEAKER 3 Well, I mean, I think being the eldest child is, um, the hardest position in the family to be, really. Um, I think it's because, I think you feel like you're sort of a pioneer in the family because you have to sort of establish the rules and how it's going to, how it's going to work, and so you have lots of rows and especially when you're a teenager which, um, I think, I know my younger sisters, um, didn't have. They sort of got all the advantages of the, the battles that I was fighting about how late to stay out and all that sort of thing. Um, and I suppose I resented them for that, in a way. But I think if you are the first child, you get more attention and I think you are, you can get quite spoilt – until they come along, that is. Um, and I know they say that, um, the eldest children quite often go on to become leaders, um, I don't think I will, but we'll see.

SPEAKER 4 Well, it's generally supposed to be the best position in a family, but, er, I don't entirely agree with that. I know that I certainly was spoilt, but, er, I don't think that's a good thing really. I've got two older brothers and all I can really remember is fighting with them. Oh, but there was one advantage. And that was that they'd done all the hard work, really, so, when I was a teenager, my parents had more or less given up; and I was allowed to do what I liked. That was a definite advantage; it gave me more freedom. But, one thing, um, I didn't like was all the clothes that were handed down to me. I never seemed to get anything new – which I thought was decidedly unfair. Um, and they say that the youngest child has more chance of following an artistic career. And that's certainly true in my case – I'm a graphic designer, and my two older brothers are accountants.

Lesson 3 **Listening, activity 2**

SPEAKER 1 Stage four from Alençon to Le Havre finishes in dramatic fashion for Tour leader, Laurent Jalabert. An accident 2 km from the finish cost him 50 seconds. Jalabert collided with another cyclist and fell. He wasn't injured, but was seriously shaken by the fall.
In Belgium, the 7th stage from Charleroi to Liège becomes a demonstration of Miguel Indurain's phenomenal strength. The Spaniard, winner for the last four years, establishes a 50-second gap between himself and his closest rival, Switzerland's Toni Rominger, when he finishes second and keeps the yellow jersey. Stage eight is a 54 km individual time trial, one of Indurain's strongest disciplines.

SPEAKER 2 At the Mayhem Country Club in County Kilkenny on the final day of the Bowen Cup series, America's Helen Pierce on 8 under par has the chance to take the outright lead ahead of four other players. She misses a putt and finishes 11 under par and is forced into a play off with England's Jenny Clark and Mary Stuart. The 28-year-old former US amateur champion wins her second title by one stroke and moves up to second overall position in the series.

SPEAKER 3 Canada's Pete Taggert in a Ford starts from pole position in the second world championship race of the season. On lap 2, the defending champion, Jim Stuart, collides with a fellow Canadian and has to go into pits for a wheel change. On lap 34, Taggert is leading with the Brazilian, Greg Tomando, close on his tail and the German, Gunther Brek, in a Mercedes lying in third position. Taggert, who surrenders his lead only once in the race, takes the chequered flag for the third year running.

SPEAKER 4 The American, Chrissie May, gets off to a good start and is at least a metre ahead of Hungarian, Katerina Schwab at the half-way mark. Coming up to the turn, she is still leading by a head, but the Hungarian is gaining ground in the outside lane. Oh, that's a bad turn. May has lost ground and the Hungarian swimmer is coming up very strongly now. The other swimmers are all over a length behind the two leaders. It's going to be a close finish; the American is fighting to stay ahead. It looks like she touches first. Yes, first, Chrissie May for the USA, second Katerina Schwab for Hungary, and in third place, more than two lengths behind, Cleo del Marteo for Spain.

SPEAKER 5 There are eight horses through to the final jump off of the Bradley Cup here at Wembley. It's against the clock and the course is very technical. The first horse to jump is Software, ridden by Jennifer Green for Great Britain. A new horse on the international circuit this year. He has shown enormous potential. They're off and they're safely over the first gate. They're heading for the double now, very fast indeed, and they're safely through that. A sharp turn to the wall. It's a very good time indeed. Now the water and the big triple ... Oh, he touched that, but it's not down. And it's a clear round. And an excellent time to beat ...

Lesson 4 **Listening, activity 1**

MARY Right then, well, Peter, what shall, what shall we do first? What about going for, maybe going for a stroll around the town?
PETER Yeah, that'd be good. To, just to, you know, get a feel of the atmosphere.
MARY Yeah. Um, we could maybe even do a, do a sightseeing tour.
PETER Yeah. Yeah, I'd like to do that. That'd be good.
MARY Mmm.
PETER Um, oh, I, I want to go to a bar.
MARY Mmm, yes, let's do that.
PETER Just to, just to drink cheap wine and listen to flamenco music...
MARY Oh, yes, I'd love do that. And also we should go out and eat somewhere, and maybe try some local specialities.
PETER Yeah. That'd be good.
MARY Yeah.
PETER Oh, and I wanted to go to the, the flea market on Sunday morning...
MARY Oh, I didn't know about that.
PETER Yeah. I don't know. We might find some unusual souvenirs and things to take home for people.
MARY Yes! Let's do that, definitely. Oh, I tell you what I want to do as well; I want to go and see, um, go to the opera and maybe see *Carmen* or something like that...
PETER Go and see *Carmen*, yeah...
MARY ...you see, *Carmen*'s on at the moment.
PETER Yeah, yeah, yeah, I wouldn't mind doing that.
MARY Yeah.
PETER Um, but I also, I mean obviously I've got tickets for, to see Real Madrid, yeah, playing at the, the football stadium. I know you don't want to do this.
MARY No, no, I really don't want to do that, no.
PETER But it's, you know, it's famous; it's the famous Santiago de Bernabéu Stadium, I means it's...
MARY Yeah, OK, OK... Well, we can discuss that later. But I tell you what we have to do is go to the, the, er, the Prado, the art gallery. Because there's lots of paintings

by Velásquez and Goya. So I'd really like to do that. Do you want to do that?

PETER Yeah, I do. But I also want to go to the, er, the Centro de Arte Reina Sofia. You know, the contemporary art gallery.

MARY Oh, yes!

PETER Because there's lots of, um, Picasso's works in there, which I'd like to see.

MARY Oh, and you know the other thing is, um, this is something I read about, which is the, er, the Strawberry Train, which goes from Atocha Station to Aranjuez. And I'd really like to do that. Will you, will you come with me on that?

PETER On the Strawberry Train?

MARY Yeah.

PETER Yeah, OK, sure. Well, yeah, yeah. But I also, I mean, I want to have, to be honest, I want to have a siesta at some point.

MARY Oh, well, yes, of course.

PETER Before we go on the Strawberry Train.

Lesson 5   Listening, activity 2

SPEAKER 1 Every time I see a sunset, um, it, I remember the past and being at school and, er, I remember once being on Runcorn Heath and looking out over a really, really beautiful sunset, and, er, I really think it was one of the most romantic moments of my life. Just that feeling of just feeling really well, contented.

SPEAKER 2 I don't know what it is about sunsets, but whenever the sun dips down, I, I always, I'm very aware of the passing of time. And I can't help thinking that another day's gone and I haven't done a lot yet, and things like that. And that makes me quite kind of melancholic in a, in a funny kind of way. And, er, it's a kind of mixture of, of, of longing and sadness and romance – and, and pleasure as well, to be honest.

SPEAKER 3 I really like watching a sunset with a friend. It's, it's a moment I like to share with someone. Um, I think about the future, sort of watching, watching the sun go down, I think, well, that's the end of a day, that's another day gone and then, there's going to be another day tomorrow, so what's, what's going to happen then? It's a good feeling. I feel satisfied and relaxed and, if there's someone there, I feel very romantic.

SPEAKER 4 For me, there's something very spiritual about a sunset. Um, in a funny way it makes me feel very small and insignificant. Um, it makes me realise how, how tiny I am. Um, and, and, er, there's something...you know, if you're together with a group of people, a sunset unites everyone who watches it, um, and it also sort of unites the past and the present as well. It sort of brings everything together in this one magical moment. Um, I sort of, when I'm watching a sunset, I think of people and, er, I think of, er, you know, past experiences that I've had. It's a very, it's a very special, er, experience. Um, I suppose really it's just one of the best moments of the day.

SPEAKER 5 It's strange because I always look forward to sunsets. And, but then, when, when the sun goes down, I think of the inexorability of things; the fact that everything always comes to an end. Then I feel sad and I don't have happy thoughts. But I prefer sunrise. Sunrise is a much happier occasion. I prefer sunrise, but I'm too lazy to get up to enjoy it!

Lesson 6   Listening, activity 1

SPEAKER 1 Well, she's, er, she's quite tall. Actually, er, I'd say she's very tall, really. Um, she's slim and, er, rather graceful. She's got, um, shortish hair. It's, er, it's red. It's cropped quite short at the sides and, er, longer on top. Um, she's got brown eyes; um, she wears earrings sometimes. She sometimes wears glasses. And she's got a lovely broad smile.

SPEAKER 2 He's quite tall, a little taller than average. Um, medium build. Um, his hair is short, quite thick and springy – er, light brown with goldy highlights in it. Um, soft features, a rounded face and very soft, brown eyes. Um, and long eyelashes, and two quite deep dimples when he smiles.

SPEAKER 3 Um, he's got a naturally, um, outdoor sort of healthy skin complexion, but it's particularly so at the moment; he's got a lovely tan. And he's got very warm, penetrating brown eyes. Um, and a light beard and moustache at the moment – that tends to come and go. And dark hair, and he's tall and slender. Um, his hair's thinning a bit now, and he's, er, has a very relaxed, easygoing way with him.

SPEAKER 4 She's got long, dark brown hair that's slightly frizzy and tied in a bunch at the back. She's got, um, greeny-brown eyes, um, a very attractive smile. She's of medium height, I would say, slim, um, very attractive, um, palish complexion, um, and a very neat, small nose.

Lesson 7   Listening, activity 1

SPEAKER 1 The most beautiful view that I can recall was in China. I remember we were cycling with a group of tourists. Um, it was one of those guided tours that take you into the remote country areas. We had been cycling through some pretty monotonous flat country, when we came to an area of small wooded hills. It, it was hard pedalling, but when we reached the brow of the hill, there was a wonderful view of the paddy fields. They had been built on the slope of a hill, one below the other, so that they could be flooded. There were firs and bamboos growing in the hollows. They looked as if they had been planted by a skilful gardener. There was an extraordinary sense of ordered beauty, as if the whole scene was an imitation of nature. It was like a painting. It was unbelievably beautiful. Not spectacular, but soft and gentle. The little hills rising up behind one another out of the mist gave the impression of something out of a dream.

SPEAKER 2 I remember the first time I flew over the Alps. It was extraordinary, breathtaking. There were a few clouds clinging to the mountain slopes. They looked like little wads of cotton wool floating about in the wind. Although it was summer, some of the higher peaks were covered in snow and there were lakes which looked like polished mirrors. Many of the mountains looked wild and remote and there were vast, dark forests covering many of the middle slopes, stretching up as far as the snowline. On the lower slopes there were meadows, and I could see rivers gently winding their way through the valleys. I could clearly make out the small towns and villages which were mainly in the valleys, and the roads and fields made the lower parts look more hospitable. Sometimes a small road would wind its way up a mountain and come to an end at an isolated farm building. We were too high up to be able to make out cattle in the fields or cars.

SPEAKER 3 The south coast of France seen from the sea is certainly the most breathtaking view I have ever seen. Er, I remember seeing it for the first time when I sailed back from Corsica. It was late in the afternoon and the sun was setting. And in the foreground was the sea – a long strip of deep blue with a little white fringe along the sea edge. Above the sea was a narrow strip of land, but we were too far out to sea to make out any details. Then there were clouds. Long, misty tongues of dreamy white, hungrily licking the land. Then rising out the clouds were the magnificent mountains. They dominated the whole picture and made me feel very small. It was like a painting, and there was, there was no movement. Everything appeared vertical and without depth. The whole scene was magical and I bring it to mind whenever I am somewhere ugly and unpleasant.

Lesson 8 **Listening, activity 1**

WOMAN Oh, he certainly seemed very upset this morning. Perhaps we shouldn't have left him alone last night. I hope he's not going to start seeing things in the dark when we get back home.

MAN So do I. I hope it was just the heat and the strange surroundings. I couldn't stand it if his mind started to slip. Who'd have thought that dad could actually believe there was a ghost in his bedroom? He's always made fun of people who believe in ghosts. Well, I suppose we'd better go and tidy the room now he's gone back home. I do hope he'll be all right on his own.

WOMAN Don't worry. There are no changes and he knows the station like the back of his hand. He'll get a taxi back home. Come on, let's get that room done.

MAN Heavens! The bed looks like a battleground! He must have had a really bad night.

WOMAN Aah! Steve! Come and look at this! Oh, oh, how horrible!

MAN What is it? Good God! How on earth did that get there?

WOMAN Look! Over there, behind the chair, there's a gap in the floorboards. It must have got in through there. Oh, how awful! Your poor dad! I feel so ashamed of making fun of him and his funny noises in the night. Thank goodness Granta was with him. I mean, it might be a poisonous snake for all we know. It must have been so awful, knowing there was something there but not being able to see it. Ugh! It's disgusting! Do you think it escaped from a zoo or something?

MAN It looks like a cobra to me. They're dangerous enough. Anyway, it can't do any harm now, it's completely mangled. It looks as if it was bitten *and* beaten to death.

WOMAN I suppose Granta must have attacked it. I didn't know dogs would attack snakes. But it does look as if it was hit by something too. Do you think we should tell him?

MAN I don't think so, do you? He's probably forgotten all about it by now. It might upset him even more than the idea of having been in a room with a ghost.

Lesson 9 **Listening, activity 1**

SPEAKER 1 It's odd, you know, because, um, I can't remember very much about my first year at school, but I remember very clearly the first time I went to kindergarten. My mum drove me there in the morning, and I think I was only supposed to stay a few hours – anyway that's what she told me later. Well, I can clearly recall the place. We went up an outdoor staircase with a sort of concrete balcony at the top. There was, there was a glass door with another half door leading into the main room. I can still picture a big, bare room with toys scattered on the floor. I, I can't recall there being any other children there, but I suppose there must have been. Anyway, mum stayed for a bit and played with me and then she left. Oh, I remember that moment as clearly as if it was yesterday. I ran to the door at the top of the steps and hung on to the handle, screaming and sobbing hysterically. I have no idea how long I stayed there, but it seemed like forever. Anyway, then mum came to fetch me and I never went back there again.

SPEAKER 2 I'll never forget my first riding lesson at school. I must have been four or five perhaps. We had to choose between riding and piano. I chose riding. I recall the journey to the riding stables. I was tremendously excited. A lady called Mrs Jenkins came to fetch us in a sort of mini-bus and she took us to her farm a few miles away. She was a very loud lady, but very friendly and I don't recall being at all frightened. Then I tried on riding hats until I found one my size. I can even remember the feel of the elastic under my chin and the marvellous smell of the saddles. I can't remember much about the ponies on that first day, but I can clearly recall being covered in mud when I got home. I can also remember enjoying that very much too! It is one of my most vivid memories and I'm sure that wonderful first impression made me fall in love with riding.

SPEAKER 3 I have a very blurred memory of my first day at school, so I suppose it can't really have upset me very much. What I remember most were the new smells, and in particular, the smell of my new blouse. It was a sort of soft cotton with a very distinctive smell. I can also recall struggling to do up my tie. Apart from that, I can't even picture my teacher's face or those of the other children. One particular memory has stuck in my mind, and unfortunately it set me against the school for a long time. One morning, when the bell went, the headmistress called us all into assembly and held up an empty bag of sweets. She waved it about and then said that she had left it on the hall table and someone had stolen the contents. She said that she knew who the culprit was and would give her two minutes to own up. Everyone went very quiet. Nobody said a word. Then, she called me out to the front, grabbed my arm and said to the rest of the school that not only was I a thief, but I was also a coward. I remember being completely bewildered and humiliated. I couldn't believe what was happening to me. I had never stolen anything in my life and I couldn't understand why she was accusing me of stealing the sweets. From that day I hated her and the school.

Lesson 10 **Listening, activity 1**

News item 1

SPEAKER 1 And now football. Two top football players have been convicted of match-fixing.

SPEAKER 2 After a trial lasting over one month, the court today found Mitch Humber and John Mint guilty of corruption and conspiracy for accepting gifts of cash to rig matches.

Throughout the case, the players consistently denied the charges and the suspended jail sentence came as a shock to them. The court did not enforce a ban from playing on the two men, but said that that was a matter for the club and the Football Federation to deal with. A spokesman for the Football Federation said that it is likely to make an example of the case and ban Humber and Mint for life. A businessman also suspected of being involved in the match-rigging has been charged with conspiracy. The case will be brought before the courts in February.

Humber and Mint's solicitor told reporters that they would be appealing against the sentence.

News item 2

SPEAKER 1 The High Court has sentenced a former car dealer from Dreadford to a £2000 fine and a court order to keep the peace for libel and harassment of his neighbours.

SPEAKER 2 The court was told that Alan John littered the village with abusive signs libelling his neighbour, Peter Fortenham, a retired managing director. The signs were part of a calculated and long-lasting hate campaign. The three-year feud began when Mr John moved into the house next door to the Fortenham family and immediately replaced a wooden fence with a brick wall. When the Fortenhams got back from holiday, they found what was left of the fence lying on their lawn and a six-foot wall between the two gardens. Soon after the incident, Mr John started putting up notices around the village libelling Mr Fortenham. He accused his neighbour of killing his daughter's dog with a fork and he also claimed that Fortenham threatened to hire a hit-man to kill his youngest son.

Mr John's solicitor said that the sentence was grossly unfair and that his client was considering an appeal. He maintained that he was the victim and that the allegations were unfounded.

News item 3

SPEAKER 1 A road rage driver has been jailed today. Chris Jones has the story.

SPEAKER 2 A company chief from Reading was jailed for three months at Greenway Court, north London today. Mr Hunter was given the jail sentence for head-butting another driver in an outburst of road rage. Mr Hunter, who denied the charge of grievous bodily harm, was found guilty by the court of attacking Philip Griffiths. The incident occurred when Hunter's car was involved in a minor collision with Mr Griffiths' van in west London last year. After the collision, Mr Griffiths left his van to speak to Hunter, who shouted at him to get back in and get out of his way. When Mr Griffiths refused, Hunter head-butted him and knocked him to the ground before driving off. On sentencing Hunter, the judge, Henry Butler, said that unfortunately this sort of incident, which had been called 'road rage' by the media, was becoming increasingly common. It was not the first case he had come across of drivers attacking other drivers who have, for some reason, incurred their displeasure.

Lesson 11 **Listening, activity 1**

WOMAN Come and look at this catalogue, Pete. I got it through the post this morning. There are some really wacky things in it – great for Christmas presents!

MAN Oh. What on earth is that? 'World's first microchip-controlled Home Drinkscentre. Dispenses gin and tonic at the touch of a button. £149.99'.

WOMAN You've got to be mad to spend time inventing a stupid thing like that. It's so easy and more fun to prepare drinks yourself. I certainly wouldn't waste money on one, and I can't think of anyone we know who would appreciate one in their home. And how about this: 'The CZ704 Scrabble Computer. Simply tap in your seven letters and within seconds the 40-megabyte RAM chip' – whatever is that? – 'will give you on-screen access to all possible combinations to achieve maximum score value. Reduces playing time to ten minutes.'

MAN Hey, I wouldn't mind one of those! Anything to shorten the never-ending games with the kids. I could hide it under the table, couldn't I?

WOMAN Don't be rotten. You only play a couple of times a year. It would be ridiculous to buy one. Well, I'm not getting you one of them for your Christmas present. Hey, now, this is more in your line – glowing pyjamas! It would be easy for me to keep an eye on you when you sleepwalk if you had a pair of those.

MAN The trouble is, they'd probably keep us both awake! What about an electronic crossword solver? That's even better than the Scrabble Computer! Let's see. No, I don't see much point in that: 'The ultimate aid for crossword puzzlers, this new pocket computer is an essential for all crossword addicts. When stuck for an answer, enter the letters you know and a question mark for those you don't. In seconds, Crossword Solver fills in the blanks. Only £49.99.' – That's a good one for your Auntie Annie. It would be really useful for her to have one. She's always driving other people mad with her crosswords.

WOMAN I fancy this alarm clock with no face or hands. It would be fun to have one. I'm not sure what the point of it is, though, but it's attractive looking, which is more than you can say for the rest of the stuff in the catalogue. I wish they'd invent something really useful, something we really need.

Lesson 11 **Sounds, activity 2**

1 It would be really useful for her to have one.
2 It would be easy for me to keep an eye on you.
3 It's kind of you to invite us for the weekend.
4 It's essential for her to get a good grade in her exams.
5 It's very thoughtless of him to forget your birthday.
6 It's important for her to spend time with her grandchildren.
7 It's generous of you to bring them presents.
8 It's careless of them to lose the book.

Lesson 12 **Listening, activity 1**

1

MAN So, what's the most unusual restaurant you've ever been to?

WOMAN Oh, a really extraordinary place called Jurassic Nosh. My first impression of the place was a bit off-putting. It looked like the last place on earth where you were likely to get a good meal. To start with, the building was a wooden hut. And there were animal skulls and untanned hides draped over the entrance. There was even a replica of a mummified prehistoric man in the hall. Quite disgusting! It was so weird, I half expected to find people sitting cross-legged on the floor gnawing bones. But inside it was really cosy, with lots of interesting old things scattered about. There was an incredible collection of fossils and all sorts of old tools and things.

MAN What about the food? Was it as unusual as the surroundings?

WOMAN It didn't look very nice, that was the main problem. In fact, it wasn't at all appetising to look at. But it was extremely tasty when I got over the shock of the way it looked. There were some really strange things on the menu – deer's tail served with nettles and dandelions, grilled radishes, funny soups ...

MAN What did you have?

WOMAN Um, I had a dish called *spelt soup,* served in a bowl made of bread. Spelt is an ancient form of wheat which Neolithic man was supposed to eat. It was delicious but very filling. And then I had a dessert made with berries and honey which was excellent.

MAN Well, it certainly sounds unusual!

2

WOMAN How did you become interested in exotic cooking?

MAN Well, Dutch cooking is very traditional and I wanted to offer customers something different, something unusual. I wanted to create something new. Here in Rotterdam we are very lucky because there is one of the biggest food markets in Europe. You can buy anything here from chicken and beef to kangaroo and ostrich meat. There are about 300 different sorts of fruit and shellfish on sale from all over the world. So you see there is plenty of scope for the imagination.

WOMAN So, tell me about Snake Bar. Um, is it, is it in the market?

MAN No, not in the market, but very near. I specialise in, er, strange food. You won't find chicken or pork on the menu. The menu varies quite a bit. It depends on what is in season. There is always a dish of the day and a number of basics. A very popular dish which is on the menu all year round is marinated sea bear with fresh ginger. Alligator is another great favourite, especially with the children. It's also possible to order a meal in advance. That's always a good idea if you want to eat something very rare.

WOMAN And what sort of clientele do you get?

MAN Oh, all sorts of people. Most people come for an unusual evening out and are ready to try almost anything. But I get a lot of people who work at the market coming in at midday. I do fresh snake sandwiches and ostrich salad at lunchtime.

3

WOMAN How long have you been running the Rigoletto?

MAN Um, over three years now, when I came to Brussels. Before then, I worked in Italian restaurants all over – in Italy, France, Britain and America.

WOMAN What gave you the idea of choosing the menus for your customers?

MAN I realised that certain types of people preferred certain types of food. It became easy to anticipate what they would order. It was a sort of game until it occurred to me that I could use the idea in a restaurant of my own. So I opened the Rigoletto with my brother who is a chef.

WOMAN And how do you go about choosing the menus?

MAN Ah. I chat with customers for a few minutes, but not necessarily about food. This gives me an idea of the sort of person they are. Um, another important factor is gender. Women are milder, more subtle; they are fond of rich, creamy sauces, while men like their food spicier, more lively; they seem happier when food is cooked in olive oil and served with plenty of the juices from the meat. Even vegetables are gender-biased. Men like the stronger tastes like artichokes and aubergines; women prefer cauliflowers and, er, courgettes.

WOMAN Oh. And do you ever get it wrong?

MAN I once served tuna to a man who ate the whole dish, said it was delicious and asked what it was. When I told him it was tuna, he said he couldn't believe it – he hated tuna. So, I don't just surprise people, I make them discover their own tastes.

4

WOMAN I went to a really great place last night: Big George, near the supermarket. It doesn't look much from the outside, but there's a great atmosphere and it's amazing value for money, provided you are a big eater like us. There's only one menu. Um, you pay £20 and you eat as much as you like. Of course, if you're not very hungry, it's perhaps not a very good idea to go there.

MAN What's the food like?

WOMAN Not bad at all. There's an awful lot of choice. They bring you a starters trolley with all sort of things on it – um, a variety of salads, salami, pâté, garlic bread, chilli beans, oh, and lots more. Then you get a main dish with vegetables – if you still have any room, that is. Personally, I ate so many starters that I didn't even contemplate the main dish. And I'd also spotted the dessert trolley as I came in, and because I've got a sweet tooth, I thought I'd better leave room for that.

MAN It sounds like they encourage people to eat so many starters and desserts that they won't want anything else.

WOMAN Yeah, I reckon that's what they do. I mean, if everyone ate everything, they would go bankrupt. And I don't think it's worth going there unless you are really hungry. It's open very late, too, which is handy if you want a meal after the cinema.

MAN I'll have to try it! It sounds great.

Lesson 13 **Listening, activity 2**

WOMAN OK, take the pocket calculator, that was the first widespread tool. It has destroyed the ability of a whole generation to do simple maths – yeah, mental arithmetic. And that means a generation of teachers who are incapable of teaching simple maths. How are we going to get that skill back?

MAN That's ridiculous! It's just a time-saver. I mean, there's so much more to learn and understand that, I mean, just using a, a calculator or any machine frees our minds. It gives us time for, to think about much more difficult and interesting things.

WOMAN OK, OK, what about the spellcheck programs on word processors? You don't have to worry about learning to write properly anymore. You just stick it down any old how and the computer will sort it out. Well, look, just imagine a teacher who can't spell or write properly!

MAN I think that that's, that's just the best development. It means that people are actually more equal now. Because somebody who, who couldn't spell at all can become the best speller in the world. We won't be judging people on the way they write, but on their ideas. And that's much more important. It's far more sensible. It's just stupid to judge people on how they spell! Look, imagine all the time you can save at school. No more, no more boring dictation exercises.

WOMAN OK. What about, what about reading, our source of culture will be the software programmers and not novelists. You know, no, in the future, it won't be novelists. Just imagine that. How can our thinking processes improve if we are all culturally the poorer and we all think the same? Already children spend more time in front of the screen and less time in books.

MAN That's just, that's just a nightmare scenario. That's just panic. These programs are all tools; they just give people more time for other more important things. Maybe reading books! Computers will never replace the human brain. They can't! We need humans to, to program them in the first place.

WOMAN Unless computers attain consciousness, then they'll be able to program themselves!

MAN Oh, never!

WOMAN No, I'm sure that isn't far off. They already make important decisions for us. These so-called networks which learn from experience. They do! They already do things like monitor drugs for patients who are very ill, or they, they even take business decisions. It's just a question of time. In a few decades we'll be asking the computers to re-teach us how to make decisions. You wait and see!

Lesson 14 **Sounds**

The Amish, who live in small, close-knit communities, are a very pious people. Their Protestant ancestors came from Europe in the sixteenth century and they have managed to preserve their customs and unique way of life. Religion is all important in their daily life and prayers are said before meals, and Sunday worship, which takes place in their homes, brings the whole community together. Amish children are not expected to marry outside the faith.

Lesson 14 **Listening, activity 1**

MAN Well, I'm glad to welcome to the studio today Mary Ann who, er, lives in Cedar Rapids in Iowa State. And if I can just, er, briefly explain that this is a town which has an ethnic Czech community which makes up about 30% of the city's population.

MARY-ANN That's right.

MAN And, um, if you go to Cedar Rapids, er, the Czech influence is obvious everywhere, but especially in the Czech quarter, the Czech village, which is a district of the town which was originally settled by immigrants, and has now been restored to its 19th-century charm. There are shops which sell traditional products such as Bohemian crystal, glass dolls, porcelain, ceramics and, er, decorated eggs. And the bakeries sell traditional breads such as houskas, is that right?

MARY ANN Yes, that's right.

MAN Which is, um, a braided raisin bread. And, um, the restaurants serve specialities such as dumplings or sauerkraut.

MARY ANN That's right, yes.

MAN And you can hear, of course, Bohemian music all over the city.

MARY ANN Yes, that's right, you've done your homework.

MAN Now, Mary Ann, where exactly do you work?

MARY ANN Oh, well, in Cedar Rapids, I am the manager of the Czech Museum and Library. And what we do there is we house the largest collection of national costumes outside the Czech Republic and Slovakia – which a lot of people don't realise. Um, we also sponsor the oldest ethnic school in the US. And we make sure that the children study the language and the culture of their grandparents, so that it lives on from generation to generation. Um, we hold Czech festivals, you know, which have traditional singing and dancing. I don't know if you know, that means sort of polkas and walzes. And I make sure that my children also know all about their traditions and their history, so that they don't forget their culture.

MAN Right. And now you yourself, were you born in Cedar Rapids or did you come over from ...

MARY ANN Um, no, I was, I was born in Cedar Rapids. My grandparents came to America in the 1840s, er, a lot of Czech immigrants came at that time. There was a great drought and, er, crop failure forced a lot of people to leave their homes. And you probably know that like a lot of other immigrants to the US, my grandparents were attracted to America because of advertisements with rumours of gold. So they were looking for a better life.

MAN And where did your grandparents live before they came over here?

MARY ANN Oh, before they arrived in the United States?

MAN Yeah.

MARY ANN They were from Moravia. They were from Moravia.

MAN Right. And, um, your children, do you tell them about life in the old country? Is it, er, important?

MARY ANN Yes, very much so. Yes, I mean, I think I mentioned before that we make sure that there's a lot of Czech festivals that are held in Cedar Rapids and that they know about what sort of food they would have eaten. So really traditions are upheld in my family, certainly, and I think within the community. Um, between that, and, um, we also try and speak the language sometimes so that they retain an interest in their ancestors. Um, we've had a lot of tourists from Europe who come over and they're amazed to find that there's a piece of their country here – in Iowa, in Iowa State.

Lesson 16 Listening, activity 2

MAN And my special guest this afternoon is Elaine Poole who is the lead violinist with the Royal Philharmonic Orchestra.

WOMAN Hello.

MAN Elaine, welcome.

WOMAN Thank you.

MAN Um, tell me, how long have you been in the orchestra?

WOMAN Um, about twelve years now, I think, yes.

MAN Twelve years? Where did you first study music?

WOMAN Er, I originally went to York University and then I sort of finished off at the Royal Academy in London.

MAN Hmmm. How old were you when you started to play the violin?

WOMAN My grandfather gave me a violin for my fifth birthday. It, er, took me a while before I could get a decent noise out of it.

MAN Yes, I'm sure. And how often do you rehearse?

WOMAN Um, well, I practise every day, personally, just for my, to keep my own technique up to scratch. But rehearsals vary according to, um, the concert schedule. Er, if you have a concert coming up, then you rehearse every day. Um, but obviously we get breaks sometimes where the work is less intensive.

MAN Right. How many musicians are there in the Royal Philharmonic Orchestra?

WOMAN Um, I think the exact number is 89, but I'm not, I'm not sure. It's thereabouts. Yes, it's a lot of people.

MAN What other instruments do you play beside the violin?

WOMAN I play, er, piano a little, not terribly well, um, sort of, I know my way around the keyboard. And flute.

MAN So, how did you choose the violin? What was it about the violin that made you want to...

WOMAN I, I think one usually ends up with an instrument that somehow reflects your own voice. Um, my voice is light, and basically I'm a natural soprano, so I think I'm naturally drawn to the, to the higher instruments, like, like the flute and the violin.

MAN Elaine Poole, thank you very much for joining us this afternoon.

WOMAN Thank you.

Lesson 17 Listening and vocabulary, activity 1

Conversation 1

MAN I've run out of cash. You couldn't lend me a few pounds until this evening, could you?

WOMAN I'm not sure I've got any either. Let's see. Oh dear! I haven't even got enough for a taxi. I'll just have to find time to get to the bank during the morning and make a withdrawal

MAN Don't take too much out because the account will be overdrawn. I got the statement yesterday and it is a bit low to say the least. That must be all the money we spent when we were away. And I haven't had time to take my pay cheque in. Oh, perhaps you could do it for me. Then we won't have to worry about the mortgage instalment on the fifteenth.

WOMAN Oh, well, I'll do my best to go in this morning. Have you got your credit card with you? Well, you can always pay for your lunch with it – and walk home!

Conversation 2

WOMAN Excuse me. Um, I want to buy a new car and I'd like some information about loans.

MAN Yes, of course. Have you got an account with our branch?

WOMAN Yes, um, a savings account and an ordinary current account. What are the interest rates on short-term loans at the moment?

MAN Well, that depends on the amount you're thinking of borrowing and over how long a period you want to pay it back.

WOMAN Well, if I have a loan for £5000, payable over three years, what will the rate be and how much will the monthly repayments be?

MAN Right. I'll get it printed out.

Conversation 3

MAN Good morning. Um, I have a savings account with your building society and I'd like to have a credit card. I believe I can withdraw cash from most cash machines?

WOMAN Yes, of course. Cash withdrawals and balance enquiries can be carried out at any machine displaying our logo. And all transactions are free of charge. But, um, it's not really a credit card because it's a savings account, so you can't use it to pay for things. It's only a cash card. We don't provide credit cards with a savings account.

MAN Oh, that's fine, it's all I need. There are machines in most places, are there?

WOMAN Yes. And where there aren't our own branch machines, there is always a cashpoint where you can withdraw money.

MAN What do I have to do to obtain a card?

WOMAN You just fill in this form and your card will be available in under ten days.

Conversation 4

WOMAN I'd like to change three hundred pounds sterling into Spanish pesetas. Could you tell me what the exchange rate is, please?

MAN Er, the buying rate has gone up slightly today and it's, um, 189.34 at the moment.

WOMAN Is it a good idea to change most of my cash here, or would it be better to do it when I get to Spain?

MAN Well, there's no need to do that. There's always the risk of it being stolen. Have you got a credit card?

WOMAN Yes.

MAN It's probably better to take it with you and you can withdraw as much money as you need anywhere. You can also pay in shops and restaurants. I'd definitely advise you not to take too much cash. It's often a good idea to take a few traveller's cheques with you in case you lose your card.

Lesson 18 Listening, activity 1

WOMAN So, Professor Taylor, thank you for coming into the studio. We, um, we have in this month's edition of *International Jupiter* a very interesting report on the state of the earth. And, er, it's raised a number of questions. And, I'd like you, if you can, to tell us what is likely to be the most major problem we'll have to face in the future, do you think?

MAN Well, er, the most alarming problem is, is still world population. You know, for the last 20 years, money has been poured into, um, family planning schemes in the third world. But in 1948, there were 2 billion inhabitants on the earth and in 1992 that figure had more than doubled to over 5 billion and by the year 2025, it's, er, it's estimated that it will have increased to over 8.5 billion. The, the failure to slow down this, this demographic explosion in developing countries, it's, it's going to be the source of enormous problems in, in every other area in the world.

WOMAN Yes, and presumably one of the things will be, well, there'll be a propensity to have more famines and, and more wars.

MAN Well, yes, of course, naturally. If the birth rate continues to increase, by the year 2025 the environment will have deteriorated so much that, um, crop growing will be even more of a problem than it is today, and famine will become, er, incredibly widespread, yes. This, of course, is likely to lead to more wars. And people will be fighting for the few resources left.

WOMAN So it's, it's really a question of the balance of power, isn't it? What do you think will determine the balance of power?

MAN Oh, things will be very much the same as they are now, I think. Energy is still likely to be the key to prosperity in the first half of the, er, twenty-first century. Twenty years ago scientists were optimistic. Er, there were going to be new sources of clean energy. But things haven't changed very much at all. We're still dependent on oil and, er, nuclear power which has created more problems with dangerous waste piling up. If we want to develop clean energy sources, money has got to be poured into international research, setting up some sort of international research fund. But, er, many countries – especially the, the richer countries – just refuse to back global energy research projects. They don't want to lose political control. Well, this is only a short-sighted policy, of course, and can only create additional problems.

WOMAN Well, thank you very much, Professor.

MAN Not at all, you're welcome.

Lesson 19 Listening, activity 1

1

Many contradictory superstitions are linked to bats. In some places they are said to be unlucky and in others they are thought to avert ill luck. In the Isle of Man and in parts of Wales, witches were said to transform themselves into bats and to enter houses where they would have power over the inhabitants. Despite this witch connection, it is thought to be extremely lucky if a bat falls on any person. In Oxfordshire, it's a death omen if a bat flies three times round a house. However, when bats come out early in the evening and fly about as they are playing, it is a sign of fine weather to come.

2

The cat has always had a very special place in folk belief. At various times and in different places, it has been regarded as a holy or a diabolical beast, as a bringer of good fortune, or as an omen of evil. In Britain, the black cat is usually considered lucky. It's a very good sign if a black cat comes into a house or on board a ship, especially if it does so uninvited. To meet a black cat is usually thought to be fortunate, especially if it runs across the path in front of you.

There are, however, many variants of these beliefs. For example, in east Yorkshire, while it's lucky to own a black cat, it's unlucky to meet one. In some places, the good fortune will only come if it is stroked three times, or greeted politely.

3

In most countries, the horseshoe is a luck-bringing, protective amulet. To find one lying in the road is very fortunate and it should not be passed by. You should pick it up, take it home and nail it over the house door. It is believed that its presence there will keep away evil and bring good fortune. There are slight variations concerning how you should hang it up: some people say the horns should point downwards, others say the opposite.

4

Almost everywhere, it is considered unlucky to walk under a ladder standing against a wall. Even today, many people avoid doing so. There are several ways of counteracting the bad luck if you can't avoid walking under a ladder. One is to cross your fingers and keep them crossed until you see a dog. Another way is to spit three times through the rungs and walk on without looking back. In some places, it was believed that to reach through the rungs for something was also unlucky.

5

It is commonly thought that to break a mirror means seven years' bad luck or else a misfortune of a particular kind, like the loss of a close friend or a death in the house. A woman could find out who would be her future husband by practising a common form of divination on Hallowe'en. She would go at night to her bedroom and light two candles on her dressing table. Then, if she stood in silence before the mirror, brushing her hair and eating an apple, she would see the face of her future husband in the glass, looking over her shoulder.

6

To open an umbrella in the house is generally said to be unlucky, and likely to bring misfortune either to the person who does it, or to the household as a whole. In some places, it's unlucky to put one on a bed. If an umbrella is unnecessarily opened during fine weather, it will bring rain. If anyone drops one, he mustn't pick it up himself, but must get someone else to do it. In some places, an umbrella is considered to be a rather ill-omened gift.

Lesson 20 Listening, activity 2

MAN Well, how did your trip go? Paris, was it?

WOMAN It was an absolute disaster. In fact, it was so bad, it was really quite hilarious. Fred saw this ad in the colour supplement which offered 'weekend breaks with a difference to the glamour spots of Europe for less than it costs to stay at home'. Well, I suppose we should have been on our guard when we read the ad. It really was too good to be true.

MAN What happened? Do tell me.

WOMAN Well, to start with, the ad said we would travel by air direct from London to Paris with a well-known airline and be met at the airport and then be taken by taxi to a luxury hotel with a view of Montmartre. Well, what it didn't say was that the flight was with an unknown charter company. We did leave from London, but we flew via Brussels where we hang around there for two hours waiting for passengers on another obscure charter flight from Bucharest. We finally landed in Paris six hours after leaving London, only to discover that our personal taxi service had turned into a coach journey.

MAN What about the hotel? Did it live up to expectations?

WOMAN You must be joking! The ad promised luxury double bedrooms with adjoining bath and toilet in a three-star hotel overlooking a unique historic area of Paris, within walking distance of some of the city's best hot spots.

MAN Sounds wonderful.

WOMAN Yeah, it was. The deception, I mean. It was a real fleapit. The sort you read about but never expect to see. 'Luxury double bedroom with adjoining bath and toilet' translates as a glorified cupboard at the end of a dark corridor with one toilet and bath for the entire floor. The sheets hadn't been changed and there were cigarette ends in the ashtrays. Not to mention no soap or towels.

MAN What about the view? Was it overlooking a derelict railway line or something even more awful?

WOMAN Even that would have been more interesting than the brick wall we could see from the window. If you climbed on a chair, you could just see the top of the dome of Montmartre – which I suppose justified the 'view of Montmartre'. And as for the hot spots. Well, I'll leave you to imagine what the neighbourhood was like!

MAN What did you do? Did you complain?

WOMAN What could we do? We had no choice. It was terribly late when we got there. No, we decided to put up with the hotel and, er, go out on the town. So we called a taxi and went to a restaurant in the Latin Quarter. And then we went on to a nightclub until the early hours. When we got back to the hotel, we were so tired that we didn't notice our surroundings. We checked out at ten and moved into a decent place for the following night.

MAN So you did have a good time in the end. But I suppose it cost a lot more.

WOMAN An absolute fortune. But we've put in a complaint and, er, we're trying to get our money back.

Lesson 6 **Reading, Activity 4**

A woman's voice behind me said: 'May I join you?' Startled, I opened my eyes and turned around. In a state of disbelief, I watched as my wife, holding a bottle of white wine and a large bag of fruit, came round and sat next to me on the bench. She looked wonderful. She'd had her hair done and was wearing a lovely floral print summer dress.

'Sandra?' I blurted out.

'I was hoping you'd come,' she smiled.

Lesson 15 **Grammar, Activity 1**

The lift started to go down. 'Yes, it's a story about how life can take a strange turn, and how bad luck and death are always around the corner when you least expect them. You see, while they're stuck in the lift, the man explains how his car was stolen several times, how his father and brother died, how his wife left him for his business partner, and how he was so depressed that he planned to blow up his partner with a bomb he had in his briefcase.' He paused.

I watched the numbers of the floors ticking away, twenty-two, twenty-one, twenty.

'Only like everything else, that went wrong. The lift got stuck, he still had the bomb in his briefcase and it was going to blow them both up. It's a great story – full of suspense.'

He smiled at me, daring me to ask him how it finished. I looked at him and at his briefcase.

Suddenly the lift stopped. The man smiled at me again in a strange way and started fumbling with his briefcase.

In a flash, I started to think about my life and how it was ridiculous to spend all this time travelling around. I only pretended to have a great time, when all I wanted to do was to stay at home and be with my family, and not in some great skyscraper of a hotel, on my birthday, alone, and stuck in a lift with this ... this strange man. Why should this be happening to me?

The doors opened on the seventeenth floor. A woman stood there with her thumb pointing upwards, as if she was hitching a lift. 'Going up?' she asked. My companion raised his hand and pointed his thumb to the floor, as if deciding our fate. 'Going down.'

The doors closed and the lift continued its descent.

Lesson 20 **Grammar, Activity 1**

1 coffee;   2 car;   3 camcorder;   4 watch;
5 exercise machine;   6 face cream;   7 underwear;
8 air conditioning;   9 emergency medical alarm;
10 colour film

Wordlist

The first number after each word shows the lesson in which the word first appears in the vocabulary box. The numbers in *italics* show the later lessons in which the word appears again.

a la carte	/æ læ kɑːt/	4
adjective	/ˈædʒɪktɪv/	1
admit	/ədˈmɪt/	20
agreement	/əˈgriːmənt/	5
agricultural	/ˌægrɪˈkʌltʃər(ə)l/	7
aisle	/aɪl/	4
album	/ˈælbəm/	16
alcohol	/ˈælkəˌhɒl/	14
alien	/ˈeɪlɪən/	19
alpha	/ˈælfə/	1
amazing	/əˈmeɪzɪŋ/	20
ambulance	/ˈæmbjʊləns/	6
amusing	/əˈmjuːzɪŋ/	15
ancestor	/ˈænsestə(r)/	14
anti-conformist		
	/ˌænti kənˈfɔːmɪst/	14
anxious	/ˈæŋkʃəs/	15
apologise	/əˈpɒləˌdʒaɪz/	20
apple	/ˈæp(ə)l/	12
appointment		
	/əˈpɔɪntmənt/	6
argue	/ˈɑːgjuː/	20
arrest	/əˈrest/	10
arson	/ˈɑːs(ə)n/	10
assembly	/əˈsembli/	18
assembly hall		
	/əˈsembli hɔːl/	9
athletics	/æθˈletɪks/	3
aubergine	/ˈəʊbəʒiːn/	12
audience	/ˈɔːdɪəns/	4
bail	/beɪl/	10
bake	/beɪk/	12
band	/bænd/	16, 19
bandage	/ˈbændɪdʒ/	6
bang	/bæŋ/	8
bank	/bæŋk/	7
baptism	/ˈbæptɪz(ə)m/	14
bark	/bɑːk/	8
baseball	/ˈbeɪsbɔːl/	3
bass	/beɪs/	16
beach	/biːtʃ/	7
beckon	/ˈbekən/	2
bell	/bel/	19
bench	/bentʃ/	9
biography	/baɪˈɒgrəfi/	16
bitter	/ˈbɪtə(r)/	8
bizarre	/bɪˈzɑː(r)/	15
blackboard	/ˈblækbɔːd/	9
blackmail	/ˈblækmeɪl/	10
bleep	/bliːp/	8
blood pressure		
	/blʌd ˈpreʃə(r)/	6

blow	/bləʊ/	2
boil	/bɔɪl/	12
boring	/ˈbɔːrɪŋ/	5, *15*
bossa nova	/ˌbɒsə ˈnəʊvə/	16
boutique	/buːˈtiːk/	1, *4*
bow	/baʊ/	2
box office	/bɒks ˈɒfɪs/	4
boxing	/ˈbɒksɪŋ/	3
breadboard	/ˈbredbɔːd/	11
bribery	/ˈbraɪbəri/	10
bright	/braɪt/	20
bring up	/brɪŋ ʌp/	5
broom	/bruːm/	11
brush	/brʌʃ/	11
buggy	/ˈbʌgi/	14
building society		
	/ˈbɪldɪŋ səˈsaɪəti/	17
bullfighting	/ˈbʊlfaɪtɪŋ/	3
bungalow	/ˈbʌŋgələʊ/	1
burglary	/ˈbɜːgləri/	10
butter	/ˈbʌtə(r)/	12
buzz	/bʌz/	8
cable TV	/ˈkeɪb(ə)l tiː viː/	13
café	/ˈkæfeɪ/	4
cake	/keɪk/	12
calm	/kɑːm/	14
camcorder	/ˈkæmˌkɔːdə(r)/	13
camera	/ˈkæmrə/	13
candidate	/ˈkændɪdət/	18
candle	/ˈkænd(ə)l/	14
canteen	/kænˈtiːn/	9
canyon	/ˈkænjən/	7
caretaker	/ˈkeəˌteɪkə(r)/	9
carrot	/ˈkærət/	12
carving knife		
	/ˈkɑːvɪŋ naɪf/	11
cash	/kæʃ/	17
cash desk	/kæʃ desk/	4
castle	/ˈkɑːs(ə)l/	19
casualty	/ˈkæʒʊəlti/	6
cathedral	/kəˈθiːdr(ə)l/	7
CD player	/ˌsiːdiː ˈpleɪə(r)/	13
CD-ROM	/ˌsiːdiː rɒm/	13
centre	/ˈsentə(r)/	4
chain store	/tʃeɪn stɔː(r)/	4
chalk	/tʃɔːk/	9
charged with		
	/tʃɑːdʒd wɪð/	10
charming	/ˈtʃɑːmɪŋ/	15
chart	/tʃɑːt/	16
chemist	/ˈkemɪst/	6
cheque	/tʃek/	17
chess	/tʃes/	3
chew	/tʃuː/	2
chisel	/ˈtʃɪz(ə)l/	11
choir	/ˈkwaɪə(r)/	16
chop	/tʃɒp/	12
chopping board		
	/ˈtʃɒpɪŋ bɔːd/	11
chord	/kɔːd/	16
Christianity	/ˌkrɪstiˈænɪti/	19
circle	/ˈsɜːk(ə)l/	4
city	/ˈsɪti/	7
clang	/klæŋ/	8
clap	/klæp/	2
classic	/ˈklæsɪk/	20
classroom	/ˈklɑːsruːm/	9

clatter	/ˈklætə(r)/	8
cliff	/klɪf/	7
clinic	/ˈklɪnɪk/	6
cloakroom	/ˈkləʊkruːm/	4
coastline	/ˈkəʊstlaɪn/	7
coffee	/ˈkɒfi/	12
coffee grinder		
	/ˈgraɪndə(r)/	11
collection	/kəˈlekʃ(ə)n/	4
colossal	/kəˈlɒs(ə)l/	20
comic	/ˈkɒmɪk/	4
complain	/kɒmˈpleɪn/	20
company	/ˈkʌmpəni/	4
composer	/kəmˈpəʊzə(r)/	16
compromise		
	/ˈkɒmprəˌmaɪz/	5
computer	/kəmˈpjuːtə(r)/	13
concerto	/kənˈtʃeətəʊ/	1, *16*
confess	/kənˈfes/	10
confident	/ˈkɒnfɪd(ə)nt/	5
confused	/kənˈfjuːzd/	15
constituency		
	/kənˈstɪtjʊənsi/	18
consultant	/kənˈsʌlt(ə)nt/	6
cool	/kuːl/	16
corkscrew	/ˈkɔːkskruː/	11
cosmopolitan		
	/ˌkɒzməˈpɒlɪt(ə)n/	14
cough	/kɒf/	8
councillor	/ˈkaʊnsələ(r)/	18
country	/ˈkʌntri/	7
course	/kɔːs/	4
crash	/kræʃ/	8
creak	/kriːk/	8
credit card	/ˈkredɪt kɑːd/	17
crime	/kraɪm/	10
crutches	/ˈkrʌtʃɪz/	6
cry	/kraɪ/	8
cuddle	/ˈkʌd(ə)l/	2
currency	/ˈkʌrənsi/	17
custody	/ˈkʌstədi/	10
custom	/ˈkʌstəm/	14
cut	/kʌt/	6, *12*
dancing	/ˈdɑːnsɪŋ/	3
deafening	/ˈdef(ə)nɪŋ/	8
delicatessen	/ˌdelɪkəˈtes(ə)n/	1
delightful	/dɪˈlaɪtfʊl/	15
delta	/ˈdeltə/	1
dentist	/ˈdentɪst/	6
department store		
	/dɪˈpɑːtmənt stɔː(r)/	4
deposit	/dɪˈpɒzɪt/	17
depressed	/dɪˈprest/	15
deputy	/ˈdepjʊti/	18
degree	/dɪˈgriː/	5
desert	/ˈdezɜːt/	7
desk	/desk/	9
devastated	/ˈdevəˌsteɪtɪd/	15
dialect	/ˈdaɪəˌlekt/	14
diary	/ˈdaɪəri/	16
dice	/daɪs/	12
diner	/ˈdaɪnə(r)/	4
dinner lady	/ˈdɪnə(r) ˈleɪdi/	9
diploma	/dɪˈpləʊmə/	5
disabled	/dɪsˈeɪb(ə)ld/	6
disappointed		
	/ˌdɪsəˈpɔɪntɪd/	15

disc	/dɪsk/	16
disease	/dɪˈziːz/	6
display	/dɪˈspleɪ/	4
district	/ˈdɪstrɪkt/	7
diverse	/daɪˈvɜːs/	14
dizzy	/ˈdɪzi/	6
drag	/dræg/	19
drama	/ˈdrɑːmə/	1
dream	/driːm/	5
drill	/drɪl/	11
drowned	/draʊnd/	19
drug dealing		
	/drʌg ˈdiːlɪŋ/	10
dustbin	/ˈdʌstbɪn/	11
e-mail	/ˈiːmeɪl/	13
earthquake	/ˈɜːθkweɪk/	19
eccentric	/ɪkˈsentrɪk/	15
ecstatic	/ɪkˈstætɪk/	15
ethnic	/ˈeθnɪk/	4
elect	/ɪˈlekt/	18
elegant	/ˈelɪgənt/	14
emergency	/ɪˈmɜːdʒənsi/	6
enthusiastic	/ɪnˌθjuːzɪˈæstɪk/	15
escalator	/ˈeskəˌleɪtə(r)/	4
essential	/ɪˈsenʃ(ə)l/	20
estuary	/ˈestjʊəri/	7
excellent	/ˈeksələnt/	20
excited	/ɪkˈsaɪtɪd/	15
exciting	/ɪkˈsaɪtɪŋ/	5, *15*
executed for		
	/ˈeksɪˌkjuːtɪd fə(r)/	10
exercise book		
	/ˈeksəˌsaɪz bʊk/	9
exhibit	/ɪgˈzɪbɪt/	4
explain	/ɪkˈspleɪn/	20
fail	/feɪl/	5
failure	/ˈfeɪljə(r)/	5
fall in love	/fɔːl ɪn lʌv/	5
family	/ˈfæmɪli/	5
far-fetched	/fɑː(r) fetʃt/	15
fare	/feə(r)/	4
farmer	/ˈfɑːmə(r)/	14
fascinating	/ˈfæsɪˌneɪtɪŋ/	15
fax	/fæks/	13
feature	/ˈfiːtʃə(r)/	16
fed-up	/fed ʌp/	15
fee	/fiː/	17
fertile	/ˈfɜːtaɪl/	7
fez	/fez/	1
fiction	/ˈfɪkʃ(ə)n/	16
field	/fiːld/	7
finest	/ˈfaɪnɪst/	20
fishing	/ˈfɪʃɪŋ/	3, 7
flat	/flæt/	7
float	/fləʊt/	19
food processor		
	/ˈprəʊsesə(r)/	13
footpath	/ˈfʊtpɑːθ/	7
forest	/ˈfɒrɪst/	7
forgery	/ˈfɔːdʒəri/	10
fork	/fɔːk/	11
fortune	/ˈfɔːtjuːn/	14
foyer	/ˈfɔɪeɪ/	4
fragrant	/ˈfreɪgrənt/	8
frantic	/ˈfræntɪk/	15
fraud	/frɔːd/	10
frown	/fraʊn/	2

Word	Pronunciation	Unit
saw	/sɔ:/	11
saxophonist	/ˈsæksəfənɪst/	16
scenery	/ˈsi:nəri/	4
scented	/ˈsentɪd/	8
school	/sku:l/	5
scissors	/ˈsɪzəz/	11
scratch	/skrætʃ/	2
screech	/skri:tʃ/	8
screwdriver	/ˈskru:draɪvə(r)/	11
sculpture	/ˈskʌlptʃə(r)/	4
seaside	/ˈsi:saɪd/	7
security system	/sɪˈkjʊərɪti ˈsɪstəm/	13
sedative	/ˈsedətɪv/	6
senate	/ˈsenɪt/	18
sentence	/ˈsent(ə)ns/	10
service	/ˈsɜ:vɪs/	4
shelf	/ʃelf/	4
shiver	/ˈʃɪvə(r)/	6
shoplifting	/ˈʃɒpˌlɪftɪŋ/	10
shrug	/ʃrʌg/	2
siesta	/sɪˈstə/	1
sieve	/sɪv/	11
sigh	/saɪ/	8
silent	/ˈsaɪlənt/	8
single	/ˈsɪŋg(ə)l/	16
sister	/ˈsɪstə(r)/	6
slap	/slæp/	8
smelly	/ˈsmeli/	8
smile	/smaɪl/	2
smuggling	/ˈsmʌg(ə)lɪŋ/	10
snack	/snæk/	4
snatch	/snætʃ/	8
sniff	/snɪf/	8
snore	/snɔ:(r)/	8
sob	/sɒb/	8
soprano	/səˈprɑ:nəʊ/	16
sour	/ˈsaʊə(r)/	8
spade	/speɪd/	11
spanner	/ˈspænə(r)/	11
sparkle	/ˈspɑ:k(ə)l/	20
speeding	/ˈspi:dɪŋ/	10
spelling	/ˈspelɪŋ/	1
spicy	/ˈspaɪsi/	8
spire	/ˈspaɪə(r)/	19
sport	/spɔ:t/	5
spread	/spred/	12
spying	/ˈspaɪɪŋ/	10
square	/skweə(r)/	7
squeeze	/skwi:z/	8
staff	/stɑ:f/	9
stage	/steɪdʒ/	4
stalls	/stɔ:lz/	4
standard	/ˈstændəd/	20
star	/stɑ:(r)/	4, 20
stare	/steə(r)/	2, 8
statement	/ˈsteɪtmənt/	17
steam	/sti:m/	12
stereo	/ˈsterɪəʊ/	13
stew	/stju:/	12
stick	/stɪk/	6
stimulating	/ˈstɪmjʊˌleɪtɪŋ/	15
stinking	/ˈstɪŋkɪŋ/	8
stone	/stəʊn/	19
stoop	/stu:p/	2
strainer	/ˈstreɪnə(r)/	11
stream	/stri:m/	7
stress	/stres/	14
stretch	/stretʃ/	2
stroke	/strəʊk/	8
stroll	/strəʊl/	4
succeed	/səkˈsi:d/	5
success	/səkˈses/	5
suggest	/səˈdʒest/	20
sunworshipping	/ˈsʌnˈwɜ:ʃɪpɪŋ/	19
surfing	/ˈsɜ:fɪŋ/	3
surgeon	/ˈsɜ:dʒ(ə)n/	6
surgery	/ˈsɜ:dʒəri/	6
surprise	/səˈpraɪz/	20
sushi	/ˈsu:ʃi/	1
suspect	/səˈspekt/	10
sweet	/swi:t/	8
sweet-smelling	/ˈswi:t smelɪŋ/	8
symphony	/ˈsɪmfəni/	16
tablet	/ˈtæblɪt/	6
take an exam	/teɪk æn ɪgˈzæm/	5
talent	/ˈtælənt/	5
target	/ˈtɑ:gɪt/	5
tasty	/ˈteɪsti/	20
telephone	/ˈtelɪˌfəʊn/	13
temperature	/ˈtemprɪtʃə(r)/	6, 7
tennis	/ˈtenɪs/	3
tenor	/ˈtenə(r)/	16
tense	/tens/	14
the Internet	/ði: ˌɪntəˈnet/	13
the opposition	/ði: ˌɒpəˈzɪʃ(ə)n/	18
thrilled	/θrɪld/	15
thud	/θʌd/	8
tidal wave	/ˈtaɪd(ə)l weɪv/	19
tide	/taɪd/	19
till	/tɪl/	4
tin opener	/tɪn ˈəʊpənə(r)/	11
tip	/tɪp/	4
tired	/ˈtaɪəd/	15
toaster	/ˈtəʊstə(r)/	11
tomato	/təˈmɑ:təʊ/	12
touching	/ˈtʌtʃɪŋ/	15
town	/taʊn/	7
travel	/ˈtræv(ə)l/	5
trespass	/ˈtrespəs/	10
trial	/ˈtraɪəl/	10
tricky	/ˈtrɪki/	20
tropical	/ˈtrɒpɪk(ə)l/	7
trout	/traʊt/	12
tweezers	/ˈtwi:zəz/	11
uncertain	/ʌnˈsɜ:t(ə)n/	5
unemployment benefit	/ˌʌnɪmˈplɔɪmənt ˈbenɪfɪt/	17
uneventful	/ˌʌnɪˈventfʊl/	15
university	/ˌju:nɪˈvɜ:sɪti/	5, 7
unspoilt	/ʌnˈspɔɪlt/	7
upset	/ʌpˈset/	15
valley	/ˈvæli/	7
VAT	/ˌvi: eɪ ti:/	17
vegetation	/ˌvedʒɪˈteɪʃ(ə)n/	7
verb form	/vɜ:b fɔ:m/	1
Victorian	/vɪkˈtɔ:rɪən/	4
video recorder	/ˈvɪdɪəʊ rɪˈkɔ:də(r)/	13
village	/ˈvɪlɪdʒ/	7
vineyard	/ˈvɪnjɑ:d/	14
volume	/ˈvɒlju:m/	16
vote for	/vəʊt fə(r)/	18
wages	/ˈweɪdʒɪz/	17
ward	/wɔ:d/	6
warn	/wɔ:n/	20
washing machine	/ˈwɒʃɪŋ məˈʃi:n/	13
water	/ˈwɔ:tə(r)/	12
waterfall	/ˈwɔ:təˌfɔ:l/	7
watering can	/ˈwɔ:tərɪŋ kæn/	11
wave	/weɪv/	2
wealthy	/ˈwelθi/	14
weapon	/ˈwepən/	10
west	/west/	7
wheelchair	/ˈwi:ltʃeə(r)/	6
whisper	/ˈwɪspə(r)/	8
whistle	/ˈwɪs(ə)l/	8
wild	/waɪld/	20
windswept	/ˈwɪndswept/	19
wink	/wɪŋk/	2
withdrawal	/wɪðˈdrɔ:əl/	17
wonderful	/ˈwʌndəˌfʊl/	20
wood	/wʊd/	7
word order	/wɜ:d ˈɔ:də(r)/	1
worried	/ˈwʌrɪd/	15
wound	/wu:nd/	6
wrong word	/rɒŋ wɜ:d/	1
yawn	/jɔ:n/	2
yoga	/ˈjəʊgə/	3

Wordbank

Use the categories below to help you to organise new vocabulary. Try to write each new word in at least two different categories. You may also like to write down words which often go with the new vocabulary items.

character	clothes	countries and nationalities
crime and justice	customs and traditions	daily life
days, months, seasons	education	environmental issues
family and friends	food and drink	geographical features and locations
health and physical feelings	house and home	language learning
leisure interests	the media	parts of the body
personal information	personal possessions	physical appearance
politics, government and society	religion	shops and shopping
social situations	town features and facilities	transport
travel	work	weather

Heinemann English Language Teaching
Halley Court, Jordan Hill, Oxford OX2 8EJ
A division of Reed Educational & Professional
Publishing Limited

OXFORD MADRID FLORENCE ATHENS PRAGUE
SÃO PAULO MEXICO CITY CHICAGO
PORTSMOUTH (NH) TOKYO SINGAPORE
KUALA LUMPUR MELBOURNE AUCKLAND
JOHANNESBURG IBADAN GABORONE

Heinemann is a registered trademark of Reed
Educational & Professional Publishing Limited.

ISBN 0 435 24017 X (without Key)
    0 435 24029 3 (with Key)

Text © Simon Greenall 1996
Design and illustration © Reed Educational and Professional
Publishing Ltd 1996

First published 1996

Designed by Giles Davies

Cover design by Stafford & Stafford

Illustrated by Mike Atkinson, Phil Bannister, Jerry Collins,
Peter Cornwell, Ed McLachlan, Julian Mosedale,
David Simmonds, Gary Wing

Acknowledgements

The publishers would like to express their thanks to the
following for permission to reproduce copyright material:
Steve Chaloner for 'The Anniversary' from *The European
Magazine* (12–18 October 1995, No. 283), copyright Steve
Chaloner 1995; *The European* for 'How do I do? How do I
do what?' by Fiona Rolls (*Magazine*, 19–25 October 1995,
No. 285), 'What do you think about when watching the sun
set?' (*Magazine*, 21–27 July 1995. No. 271), 'Aerobic
pedalling can help your natural cycles' by Tessa Thomas
(*Magazine* 30 June–6 July 1995), 'Mammoth joys of eating
with Otzi' by Rossella Lorenzi (*Magazine* 7–13 April 1995),
'Something new or tried and true' by Isabel Conway (*Elan*,
4–10 March 1994), 'You eat what you are' by Darius Sanai
(*Magazine*, 3–9 March 1995), 'Humans spar with silicon
superbrains' by Cliff Jones (*Magazine*, 24 February–2 March
1995), 'Villagers adapt to laboratory life' by David Bartal (3–6
June 1993), 'Five things that will change your life' by Charles
Jennings (Elan, 10–16 June 1994), 'And now, in lieu of graffiti
– loo ads' by Mindy Ran (*Magazine*, 26 May–1 June 1995);
Express Newspapers plc., The Canadian Press and Associated
Press for extracts from *Fortean Times* (April 1995, No. 80);
Greene & Heaton Ltd for 'You and I are About to Die' by Bill
Bryson, copyright 1991 Bill Bryson; *The Independent* for 'The
Weasel' (*Magazine*, 22 February–2 March 1995, No.247);
Lonely Planet Publications for the section on Patagonia from
'South America on a shoestring' (page 130); Murray Pollinger
Ltd for excerpts from *Boy: Tales of Childhood* by Roald Dahl
(Jonathan Cape/Penguin Books); *The Observer* for 'Patrick
Marber looks at his 30 years with few regrets' (18 September
1994), 'Protocol: a guide to modern living: how to hold a
dinner party' (27 February 1994), 'High-tech disaster threatens
police computer systems' by Robin McKie and Richard Sharpe
(15 November 1992); OMNI for 'Space: Where No Law Has
Gone Before' by Susan Karlin (April 1993) copyright 1993
OMNI Publications International Ltd; Reed Consumer Books
for an excerpt from *The Lost Continent* by Bill Bryson
(Abacus Books); South Herefordshire District Council for a
section of the Wye Valley and Rural South Herefordshire
Guide and Accommodation List, 1994, copyright South
Herefordshire District Council; A P Watt Ltd on behalf of
Edith M Horsley and Christina Hole for 'Butterflies' from *The
Encyclopaedia of Superstitions* by E and M A Radford, edited
and revised by Christina Hole (Helicon Publishing); You
Magazine/Solo Syndication Ltd for 'Tips from a mean
millionaire' by Adrianne Pielou (10 July 1995)

Photographs
The authors and publishers would like to thank the
following for permission to reproduce their material: Hulton
Deutsch Collection pp 70, 71; Images Colour Library p 27;
Greg Evans International pp 15(b), 16; Science and Society
Picture Library p 41; South American Pictures p 55; Tony
Stone Images pp 15(t), 21; Telegraph Colour Library pp 14, 53

While every effort has been made to trace the owners of
copyright material in this book, there have been some cases
where the publishers have been unable to contact the
owners. We should be grateful to hear from anyone who
recognises their copyright material and who is
unacknowledged. We shall be pleased to make the necessary
amendments in future editions of the book.

Printed and bound in Great Britain by Thomson Litho, East
Kilbride, Scotland

97 98 99 10 9 8 7 6 5 4